THE INFLUENCE OF SOCIAL SUPPORT AND SOCIAL CAPITAL ON HEALTH

A review and analysis of British data

THE INFLUENCE OF SOCIAL SUPPORT AND SOCIAL CAPITAL ON HEALTH

A review and analysis of British data

Helen Cooper, Sara Arber, Lin Fee and Jay Ginn
Institute of Social Research
Department of Sociology
University of Surrey

HEA Project Team
Antony Morgan *Head of Effectiveness and Monitoring Research*
Hilary Whent *Senior Researcher*

ISBN 0 7521 1433 6

Health Education Authority
Trevelyan House
30 Great Peter Street
London SW1P 2HW
Printed in Great Britain
www.hea.org.uk

Contents

Part II. Secondary analysis of British data

Social capital for health
Preface to the series

The recently published Acheson Report on Inequalities in Health and the Government's public health strategy 'Our Healthier Nation', recognise that the solutions to major public health problems such as heart disease, cancers, mental health and accidents are complex. They will require interventions which cut across sectors to take account of the broader social, cultural, economic, political and physical environments which shape people's experiences of health and wellbeing.

A major challenge is how to influence these broader determinants of health in such a way that relative inequalities in health can be addressed.

Recent evidence suggests that social approaches to the organisation and delivery of public health may have considerable potential for health improvement, particularly for those that suffer most disadvantage in society. The evidence base for moving forward in this field is, however, somewhat limited.

The Health Education Authority is committed to developing this evidence base and to testing social approaches to reducing health inequalities and to the promotion of health and the prevention of disease.

The HEA's first Research Strategy 1996–99 initiated a programme to investigate the concept of social capital and to establish the empirical links between aspects of social capital such as trust, reciprocity, local democracy, citizenship, civic engagement, social relationships, social support, and health outcomes, access to services, information and to power.

Social capital serves as one coherent construct which will allow us to progress the debate and discussion about the general importance of social approaches to public health and health promotion. It is however only one part of an approach to health improvement, which must also clearly embrace structural changes.

The HEA's new programme of Social Action Research in two city sites will build upon the evidence produced thus far, to demonstrate the effectiveness of a range of integrated social approaches, implemented through collaborative initiatives by local authorities, health authorities and the voluntary sector.

The early work on social capital will also feed into new in-depth analyses of social networks and citizen power and their importance to health by gender, age, ethnicity and further explore its relationships to health and inequality in individuals and in populations.

Over the coming year the HEA will be publishing a series of reports summarising the initial results of the exploratory work on social capital and its links to health.

This report presents the results of research commissioned by the HEA to exploit more fully the data already available in national datasets. The recommendations made by Helen Cooper and colleagues provide important pointers, for both the future collection of data and the generation of new hypotheses relating to inequalities in health.

Professor Pamela Gillies
Director of Research
Health Education Authority

Foreword

The Health Education Authority (HEA) is committed to tackling inequalities in health in both its corporate and research strategies, and is currently engaged in a programme of research to investigate the links between health and wellbeing and the wider determinants of health. The relative influence of structural variables and of individual behaviour on health has been extensively researched (Drever and Whitehead, 1997; Townsend, Davidson and Whitehead, 1988; Wilkinson, 1996). However, far less is known about how social support might influence health and health-related behaviour.

As part of its overall research strategy, the HEA commissioned a secondary analysis of several large datasets, reported in Part II. The aim of this research project is to analyse the relationship between social support, health-related behaviour and health. The research project examined how health status and health-related behaviours – for example, diet, exercise, smoking and alcohol consumption – are influenced by factors such as stress, and access to emotional and practical support.

Prior to the secondary analysis, a literature review of the links between health, health behaviour and social support has been carried out, and is reported in Part I. This review includes an investigation of recent literature dealing with the impact which 'social capital' – that is, the characteristics of the social environment – has upon individual and collective wellbeing.

Acknowledgements

The authors would like to thank Antony Morgan and Hilary Whent from the Health Education Authority for commissioning this research and for their helpful comments and support. Thanks are also due to Christine Callum, the Data Archive and Manchester Computing Services for access to the data-sets used in this report.

PART I

A review of the literature

Lin Fee, Sara Arber, Jay Ginn and Helen Cooper

Summary of findings from the literature

Most research on social support deals with the ways in which individuals' social resources influence their health and wellbeing, notably support from members of their social network, such as friends, family and neighbours. More recently, however, there has been increasing emphasis on investigating the links between health, health-related behaviours and levels of 'social capital' – that is, the collective social resources to which the family, neighbourhood or community has access. The key findings of the literature review are summarised as follows:

Social support

- Stress can have negative effects on mental health, leading, for example, to depression. Social support is believed to 'buffer' the individual against stress, or to enable him or her to cope with its effects.
- Although it is widely believed that stress has a negative effect on physical health, and that ill health can cause stress, the mechanisms whereby this occurs have not been identified. The negative effects of stress on physical health may be mediated by poor health-related behaviours, such as increased smoking, or may be caused by physiological factors, such as reduced immune response.
- Levels of stress have been found to be higher when individuals feel themselves to be depressed or socially isolated, and perceive low levels of available support.
- Social support can have beneficial effects on health regardless of whether the individual is suffering stress or not. Conversely, a lack of social support can lead to increased risk of mental health problems, such as depression, regardless of whether the individual experiences stress or not.
- There is evidence to suggest a relationship between social support and physical health which is mediated by health-related behaviour.
- Support from friends, family and health professionals can enhance physical health by encouraging health-promotion behaviour and discouraging poor health-related

behaviours, such as over-eating. Conversely, lack of positive support – especially where there is negative pressure from other members of the social network – can lead to over-indulgence in risky behaviours, such as smoking, or undermine the individual's attempts to practise health-promoting behaviours, such as taking up exercise.

- The larger and more diverse an individual's social network, the more access he or she will have to functional social relationships, and the more potential benefits there are likely to be for health.
- Social network size, degree of network participation and levels of perceived support increase with socioeconomic status, and for those who are in paid employment, but decrease with age.
- Social support may have a more positive effect on health and health-related behaviour, especially in times of stress, if it is provided by people of the same gender, age, ethnicity and socioeconomic background, or by people who have shared similar life-experiences.

Social capital

- There is a consensus in recent literature that the construct of 'social capital' may be usefully applied to the study of health and health-related behaviour. Researchers have measured social capital in terms of the social, collective, economic and cultural resources available to a family, neighbourhood or community.
- In addition, some researchers have measured the social, personal, economic and cultural capital of individual members of the family in studies of educational attainment and child development, for example, their access to membership of community organisations.
- Nevertheless, there is – as yet – no firm agreement among researchers as to the exact components of social capital, although a number of international meetings and conferences have taken place dedicated to producing a universally acceptable working definition of the concept.
- At present, the majority of researchers accept Putnam's definition of social capital, that is, the 'features of social life such as networks, norms, and social trust that facilitate co-ordination and co-operation for mutual benefit' (1995, p. 67). Thus, a social group with a high level of social capital is likely to be cohesive and to have well-developed networks of communication and mutual support.
- The most commonly used measures of social capital are civic participation – for example, membership of community organisations – and social trust, both of which are measured in national surveys in the USA but not, as yet, in similar surveys in the UK.
- Using US survey data, recent epidemiological research has demonstrated a correlation between low levels of social capital and mortality that is mediated by income inequality. Income inequality is thought to damage social cohesion and integration, thus leading to lack of social support within the community, characterised by social isolation, which, in turn, contributes to premature mortality.

1. Introduction

A review of the literature relating to stress, social support and social capital has been carried out in order to provide background information for a secondary analysis of three large datasets, the HEA Health and Lifestyle Surveys (1992 and 1993) (HEA, 1995), the Health Survey for England (1993–1994) (OPCS, 1996) and the General Household Survey (1994) (Colhoun and Prescott-Clarke, 1996), reported in Part II.

The aim of the research is to analyse the relationships between social support (at the individual and community level), health behaviour and health. It is hypothesised that lack of social support in times of stress can lead to poor health-related behaviours, such as increased smoking and alcohol consumption, reduced physical exercise, poor diet and self-neglect. Social support is measured by the amount and frequency of contact with social network members and in terms of the perceived quality and stability of supportive relationships. Social capital refers to the social resources of the neighbourhood and is measured by individuals' perceptions of the local environment.

The review provides definitions of terms which will be used in the analysis, and information to guide the construction of social support indices for use in the design of future Health and Lifestyle questionnaires. The utility of the concept of 'social capital' in researching health behaviour and inequalities in health is also considered.

The findings of the literature review indicate that it is necessary to give more weight to the way both 'positive' and 'negative' types of social support influence health and health-related behaviours. 'Positive' social support may encourage an individual's attempts to change his or her health-related behaviour, whereas these attempts may be undermined by 'negative' social support, for example, if family members or friends continue to smoke or drink to excess when the individual is trying to stop. In addition, the literature review suggests that health may be affected by the characteristics of the local community, such as the amount of support exchanged between neighbours, levels of group affiliation and frequency of participation in community activities.

Gillies (1997) argues that 'individualism continues to dominate many of the practical health education and disease prevention agendas, at least in industrialised countries' (p. 29). Several recent publications suggest that there needs to be a shift in emphasis from the individual's characteristics towards an investigation of the wider social, economic, environmental and cultural determinants of health (Gabbay, 1998; Gillies, 1997; Kawachi and Kennedy, 1997; World Health Organization, 1997). For this reason, the literature review distinguishes these two approaches. Chapter 2 examines research into the relationship between social support and the health of the individual; Chapter 3 examines research on the relationship between social capital and health, primarily relating to the level of the community.

At the individual level, social support refers to the companionship and the practical, informational and esteem support which derive from a person's social network. It has been theorised that the more opportunities an individual has to interact with other people, the more social support will be available, which, in turn, will have a beneficial effect on health, health-related behaviour and general wellbeing. During the past 20 years, many psychologists, sociologists and medical researchers have investigated the validity of this hypothesis and have generated a large body of literature. With the exception of epidemiological studies which link measures of social integration to longevity and mortality (for example, Berkman and Syme, 1979), studies of the effects of the amount and quality of social support on health at the individual level tend to dominate the literature. Research interest has focused on the role social support plays in promoting certain health outcomes, notably psychological wellbeing during periods of acute or chronic stress (for example, Avison and Turner, 1988; Cohen, 1988; Cohen and Williamson, 1991). There have been fewer studies of the relationship between social support and physical health (Cohen, 1988, 1989; Cohen *et al.*, 1997), or how social support may affect health behaviour (Abella and Heslin, 1984; Berkman, 1985; Cohen and Syme, 1985).

The mechanisms whereby social support affects health are complex, and are still not fully understood. For example, health affects the ability to maintain social relationships, so that a reverse causal link may occur. It has been suggested that what is lacking in social support research is an effective means of measuring levels of social support (Madge and Marmot 1987), that is, a single measure which embraces all its many properties and functions.

Recent writers have suggested that the construct of 'social capital' – that is, the social resources to which an individual has access in the community – may be important to health and health-related behaviour. Chapter 3 focuses on research on 'social capital', for example, Kawachi and Kennedy's argument that large-scale studies have failed to measure some important determinants of health:

> '. . . what has been missing from recent epidemiological studies of social

> relationships and health is the social context in which people live their lives . . . by focusing on the outcomes of socially isolated (or well connected) individuals, epidemiology has neglected the possibility that entire communities or societies might be lacking in social connections.' (1997, p. 1038)

Social connectedness – or 'social cohesion' – is generated by social network interaction. According to Kawachi, Kennedy and Lochner, it is 'the invisible glue' (1997, p. 2) which binds communities of people together, gives them a shared sense of identity and enables them to work together for the benefit of the whole community. As such, social cohesion is an elusive concept. However, a number of researchers have recently made use of the term 'social capital' to refer to levels of social cohesion at the community and societal level (for example, Putnam, 1996; Kennedy, Kawachi and Prothrow-Stith, 1996). The concept of social capital embraces all the social, collective, economic and cultural resources to which a community or population has access. Levels of social capital therefore indicate a community's potential for co-operative action to address local problems and to provide support for its members in times of need. Putnam explains social capital as follows:

> ' . . . "social capital" refers to features of social organization such as networks, norms, and social trust that facilitate coordination and cooperation for mutual benefit.
>
> For a variety of reasons, life is easier in communities blessed with a substantial stock of social capital. In the first place, networks of civic engagement foster sturdy norms of generalized reciprocity and encourage the emergence of social trust. Such networks facilitate coordination and communication, amplify reputations, and thus allow dilemmas of collective action to be resolved . . . At the same time, networks of civic engagement embody past success at collaboration, which can serve as a cultural template for future collaboration. Finally, dense networks of interaction probably broaden the participants' sense of self, developing the "I" into the "we", or . . . enhancing the participants' "taste" for collective benefits.' (1995, p. 67)

Research using social capital as a measure of social cohesion is still in its infancy, and opinions vary as to which indicators of social cohesion should be used. The majority of researchers tend to adopt those used by Putnam, Leonardi and Nanetti (1993) in their study of Italian regional governments, that is, 'levels of social trust' and 'civic activity/group affiliation' (Kennedy, Kawachi and Prothrow-Stith, 1996), but – as the literature review demonstrates – researchers have used a number of other indicators.

In the studies examined in Chapter 3, researchers have found that the higher the level of social capital – as a measure of social cohesion and co-operation – the more health benefits accrue for the members of the community concerned. The concept of social capital is therefore of particular interest to the HEA. The HEA wishes to develop a greater understanding of its properties because a number of researchers (for example,

Kari *et al.*, 1994; Putnam, 1996) suggest that projects in which social capital has been successfully used and generated – for example, in sports clubs or in agricultural co-operatives – provide 'templates' (Putnam, 1995, p. 67) for the generation of social capital in other locations and for other purposes, such as health care and health promotion. One contribution health promotion organisations like the HEA could make to addressing inequalities in health is to advise health educators about projects which use existing stocks of social capital and – in the process – generate reserves which can be put to use in other areas.

2. Social support and the health of the individual

This chapter examines literature dealing with the relationship between access to 'social support', health and health-related behaviour. In this context, social support refers to the companionship and practical, informational and esteem support which the individual derives from interaction with members of his or her 'social network', including friends, colleagues, acquaintances and family members.

In this part of the review, we examine the large and somewhat controversial body of research which focuses on conceptualising social support and investigating its role in promoting or undermining health. Research has shown that the presence or absence of social support can have a direct effect on health and mortality, and also on the health and wellbeing of those who provide emotional and practical support for others. Friends and family members may have a positive or negative influence on an individual's health-related behaviours.

In this area of research, there is a greater emphasis on psychosocial health because social support is believed to play an important role in moderating the effects of stress, particularly on mental health (for example, Brown and Harris, 1978). Assuming that an individual is cognitively aware of the stress, social support is thought to protect or buffer them against its effects (Cohen and Wills, 1985), or help them to cope with stress. We begin by assessing the role of stress in determining health and health-related behaviour.

1. Stress, stressors and strains

Thoits (citing Holmes and Rahe, 1967) has defined the terms 'stress' and 'stressor' as 'any environmental, social or internal demand which requires the individual to readjust his or her usual behaviour patterns' (1995, p. 54).

Many researchers have been concerned with identifying and differentiating between a variety of potential stressors, for example, sources of acute stress, such as bereavement (Brown and Harris, 1978; Coyne and Downey, 1991; Kessler, Price and Wortman, 1985), chronic stressors (or 'strains'), such as unemployment or work problems (Avison and Turner, 1988; Billings and Moos, 1984; Pearlin and Johnson, 1977) and more minor 'daily hassles', such as missing a train, breaking a cup or even receiving an unexpected gift (Thoits, 1995).

'Positive' and 'negative' stress

There has been some disagreement among researchers about 'positive' and 'negative' events, and whether or not these give rise to different amounts and types of stress, or affect both mental and physical health. Turner and Avison (1992) argue that the stress effects of an event depend on whether it has a positive or negative meaning for the individual concerned. In cases where the individual can find no positive meaning in an event, the severity of stress effects depend upon how well or badly he or she comes to terms with it. Brown and Harris (1978), Coyne and Downey (1991), Kessler, Price and Wortman (1985), Tausig (1983) and Thoits (1983) argue that it is negative events and experiences that are more likely to have an adverse effect, notably on mental health. Creed (1985) and Lin and Ensel (1989) claim that negative events and experiences are more likely to have an adverse effect on physical health, which may be cumulative (Cohen and Williamson, 1991).

However, Holmes and Rahe (1967) do not differentiate between positive and negative stressors; they claim that the accumulated stress effects of *all* potentially disruptive life events in a year (such as the death of a partner, starting a new job, the birth of a child and moving house) can overtax or exhaust an individual's physical and mental resources, thus making him or her more vulnerable to ill health and physical injury.

The social correlates of stress

A number of researchers have found that people from lower socioeconomic groups do not necessarily suffer more disruptive and/or unpleasant events in their lives than those with higher socioeconomic status (for example, Brown and Harris, 1978; Lin, Dean and Ensel, 1986; Turner, Wheaton and Lloyd, 1995); however, evidence suggests that they are more likely to experience chronic strain (for example, McLeod and Kessler, 1990; Turner, Wheaton and Lloyd, 1995). Disadvantaged social groups – for example, older people and those from lower socioeconomic groups – may be more vulnerable to certain types of stressor, or may suffer greater ill effects from stress (McLeod and Kessler, 1990).

Mirowsky and Ross (1989) explain these differences in reactivity in terms of the stratification system which can lead some individuals to feel that they are powerless and lack control, a hypothesis which might help to explain certain health-related behaviours, such as self-neglect. Pearlin (1989) and Reissman (1990) argue that stress is related to the individual's social roles, which, in turn, are determined by factors such as ethnicity and gender. Thoits (1987) argues that the more social roles an individual has, the larger their social network is likely to be and the more likely he or she is to suffer stress resulting from network events. However, this may be counterbalanced by higher levels of perceived social support. In terms of gender, men may be more susceptible to work-related stress and women may be more likely to suffer stress as a result of events which occur in the lives of relatives and other members of their social networks (for example, Kessler and McLeod 1984; Turner and Avison 1989).

Stress and health

According to Madge and Marmot (1987), there is a widespread intuitive feeling among researchers that a reciprocal causal relationship exists between stress and health, that is, stress can cause health problems and ill health can cause stress. However, there has been no satisfactory demonstration of the mechanisms by which causation might operate, although Orth-Gomer, Perski and Theorell (1983) and Marmot and Morris (1985) (both cited in Madge and Marmot, 1987) argue that not being able to demonstrate exactly how something works does not mean that it does not exist.

Madge and Marmot (1987) also point out that although establishing causation is difficult in every area of research, the problem is exacerbated in this case by the elusive nature of the concept of 'health', which can be measured in many different ways, for example, in terms of how well or ill the individual feels, according to the absence or presence of disease, or according to the type of disease and its perceived severity or prognosis. Using disease as a measure of health presents its own problems, since many years can elapse between the onset of a disease and its diagnosis, in which case it might be difficult for the individual to recall periods of stress from a long time before.

There has also been considerable debate amongst psychologists and psychiatrists about the characteristics of 'stress' and how it should be measured; in consequence, measures of both stress and health tend to differ from study to study. Thoits (1995) suggests that it may be difficult to establish a causal relationship simply because no one has yet found the right combination of type of stress and health outcome, or *set* of outcomes – for example, Cohen and Williamson (1991) have found that there is a relationship between depression and coronary heart disease which might be explained by stress.

The extent of knowledge about the relationship between stress and health therefore remains at the level of 'links' and 'associations' between specific types and degrees of stress and certain mental and/or physical ailments (Madge and Marmot, 1987). Cohen and Williamson (1991) suggest that links between stress and physical diseases may operate differently from those between stress and mental health problems; Ganster and Victor (1988) suggest that the link might be explained by physiological mechanisms, perhaps by a suppression of the immune system or by the 'overstimulation' (p. 26) that is caused by the body's fight-or-flight response to stress, which manifests, for example, as a rise in blood pressure.

The issue is further complicated by the host of social and economic factors which have been found to affect both levels of stress and health, for example, gender, age, ethnicity and socioeconomic status, which in turn can affect people's standard of housing, the type of environment in which they live, the type of work they do, their experience of unemployment, their lifestyle and their health-related behaviours, such as smoking or poor nutrition. Indeed, Madge and Marmot (1987) argue that some apparent links between work stress and morbidity could be the result of social factors outside the working environment. Health-damaging behaviours which have been attributed to stress – such as smoking – are also likely to be the result of social factors, such as poverty.

2. Social support

Having considered some of the ways in which stress might adversely affect health, we now examine the relationship between social support, health and health-related behaviour. Social support may affect health by moderating the consequences of stress, or may have a more direct effect on health and health-related behaviour.

This section considers how social support is defined in research literature. One of the most common criticisms of social support research is lack of consistency in terms of how it is conceptualised and measured (for example, Madge and Marmot, 1987). There appear to be almost as many definitions and measures of social support as there are studies of it, although, as this literature review demonstrates, this criticism can equally apply to the concepts of 'stress' and 'health'.

Structural and functional support

Many researchers have been concerned with identifying and labelling various types of social support, for example, differentiating between its 'structural' and 'functional' aspects (House and Kahn, 1985; Barrera, 1986; House, Landis and Umberson, 1988). The structural features of social support include the way in which social relationships are organised, for example, whether or not individuals have a 'social network' comprising a number of relatives, friends and acquaintances; how frequently they have contact with other network members; whether or not they live alone; and how often they take part in social activities. A wide range of functions have been attributed to social support, such as helping to integrate the individual into wider society; giving practical help; supplying information; enabling the recipient to express his or her feelings; bolstering the individual's self-esteem; and moderating the health effects of stress (Cohen and Wills, 1985; Kessler, Price and Wortman, 1985).

The consensus view in the social support literature is that the larger and more diverse an individual's social network, the more access he or she will have to functional relationships, and the more potential benefits are likely to accrue for health. For example, Berkman and Breslow (1983) found that an individual's risk of dying of heart disease or cancer increases as the size of his or her social network decreases; Cohen *et al.* (1997) found that the larger and more diverse an individual's social network, the greater his or her resistance to the common cold. However, both Madge and Marmot (1987) and Thoits (1995) speculate that it might be more beneficial to health and wellbeing to have only one close functional relationship than to have a large social network of unsupportive acquaintances. Hibbard (1985) argues that social network size is of less importance for those who are able to mobilise support effectively, that is, individuals who have a sense of control and who are trusting of other people.

Perceived and received support

In terms of function, researchers have identified three different types of social support – instrumental, informational and emotional (House, 1981; House and Kahn, 1985). However, these have been found to be so closely related that the key issue in terms of health tends to be whether support is 'received' in some tangible form, such as having someone listen to one's troubles, or is 'perceived' by the individual to exist, for example, whether or not he or she feels loved by a significant other or believes that emotional support would be forthcoming in times of stress. It has been found that levels of perceived support have the greatest effect on mental health (for example, Dunkel-Schetter and Bennett, 1990; Wethington and Kessler, 1986), notably when the individual believes they are under stress.

The social distribution of support

Less research interest has been shown in the social distribution of social support, but researchers have found that married people tend to report higher levels of perceived support than single people (Ross and Mirowsky, 1989; Turner and Marino, 1994) and that women tend to report slightly higher levels of perceived support than men. Thoits (1987) has found that the more social roles an individual has, the larger his or her social network is likely to be, which, while it increases the risk of stress from network events, nevertheless raises the level of perceived support.

Belle (1987) has found that women's network relationships tend to be more intensive and are thus perceived as being more supportive. Working women may be at more risk of stress as a result of having a larger network and more social roles – for example, employer, colleague, mother, spouse – but they are likely to have access to higher levels of perceived support. Flaherty and Richman (1989) suggest that women may be more sensitive to their own and others' need for support; thus, although they may be more likely to offer support to others, they may feel in need of more support themselves, which may not be forthcoming. Ginn, Arber and Cooper (1997) point out that almost half of older women (aged 65 and older) in Britain are widowed and are more likely to live alone. A key research issue is the extent to which those who live alone both perceive and receive less social support, and whether this differs between men and women.

Researchers have found that network size, degree of network participation (Thoits, 1982; Turner and Marino, 1994) and levels of perceived support (Ross and Mirowsky, 1989; Thoits, 1984) increase with socioeconomic status and for those in paid work, but decrease with age (for example, Thoits, 1984; Turner and Marino, 1994), for example, as people leave the workforce. The increasing frailty of men and women with advancing age leads to higher demand for formal practical support from statutory and voluntary agencies, and an increased need for informal support at a time of life when social networks are likely to be shrinking in size.

Social support and health

Many explanations of the link between social support and health are 'stress-centred', that is, they are based on the assumption that stress has adverse effects on health which can be prevented, moderated or cushioned by social support. However, some researchers have found that social support can have 'main' effects on health, that is, benign or beneficial effects on mental and/or physical health – measured in terms, for example, of general wellbeing or the absence of the symptoms of disease – regardless of whether the individual is suffering stress or not (Barrera, 1986; Cohen and Wills, 1985; Gottlieb, 1983;

Thoits, 1985). Conversely, according to Coyne and Downey (1991), a *lack* of social support can lead to increased risk of mental health problems, such as depression, regardless of whether the individual experiences stress or not.

Main effects of social support on health can be direct or mediated, for example, by an individual's own health-related behaviour (the relationship between social support and health behaviour is discussed below under 'Social support and health-related behaviour'). In terms of direct effects on health, Wise (1986, cited in Ginn, Arbor and Cooper, 1997) found that dealing with problems of loneliness can promote the healing of leg ulcers, and Cohen *et al.* (1997) have found that, for people aged between 18 and 55, having a large and diverse social network enhances resistance to upper respiratory tract infections, although they have been unable to discover why this should be the case. Social support might also have a direct effect on health when an individual's health needs are looked after by a relative or friend (Berkman, 1985), such as preparing nutritionally balanced meals and maintaining a clean, safe and comfortable environment. However, this does not necessarily mean that the individual will feel healthy, nor that he or she will be free from disease, or even that he or she will report a high level of perceived support.

In terms of mental health, Wills (1985, cited in Ganster and Victor, 1988) has found that the effects of stress include low self-esteem, and feelings of powerlessness and lack of personal control, which might in turn lead to depression, lack of self-care and increased susceptibility to illness. Social support may therefore enhance mental health in a number of ways, for example, by providing opportunities for interaction and help with practical tasks, thus relieving loneliness and raising levels of perceived support; by assisting the individual to cope with the 'hassles' of everyday life by giving reassurance that the individual is loved and valued, which enhances self-esteem and feelings of self-worth; by giving reassurance and feedback about the individual's competence, thus helping to restore a sense of mastery and control; and by helping the individual to reassess the nature of the stressor and to devise ways of coping or coming to terms with it (Ganster and Victor, 1988).

Much less is known about the mechanisms linking social support and physical health. Cohen and Williamson (1991) suggest that just the physical presence of a significant other may help to regulate an individual's emotional state, which in turn helps to regulate the immune system, especially in times of stress. Ganster and Victor (1988) suggest that if stress affects health through raised blood pressure or suppression of the immune system, then the beneficial health effects of social support might operate by reducing the effects of the fight-or-flight response or by strengthening the immune system. Cassell (1976) and Cobb (1976) argue that one of the ways in which social support might influence health is by enhancing resistance to disease, and Uchino, Cacioppo and Kiecolt-Glaser (1996) claim that social support has a beneficial effect on the endocrine, cardiovascular and immune systems. It is still the case that very little is known about the relationship between social support and disease onset, although there has been some research in this area (for example, Berkman and Syme, 1979; House, Robbins and Metzner, 1982). The onset of a disease might occur many years before it is diagnosed and, as in the case of stress research, it can be difficult for the individual to recall the circumstances which prevailed such a long time before, such as stressors and levels of social activity.

Social support and mortality

In their meta-analysis of social support studies, Schwarzer and Leppin (1992) found that, in comparison with people in marital relationships, twice as many single people die of coronary heart disease, and three times as many single men and twice as many single women die of pulmonary disease. They also suggest that one of the reasons why researchers have found that men are more likely than women to die in the first six months after the death of their partner (Helsing and Szklo, 1981; Ward, 1976) is that, for many men, their only close functional relationship is with their wife – indeed, for some men, their wife may be their only network member.

Men tend to be older than their wives and women tend to outlive men (Arber and Ginn, 1990, 1991). As Thoits (1982) and Turner and Marino (1994) have found, the size of an individual's network tends to decrease with age; therefore, of those who are widowed in old age, men are likely to be older, on average, than women and to have smaller networks. Consequently, men widowed in old age are less likely than widowed women to have either perceived or received support in coping with grief (for example, McGloshen and O'Bryant, 1988), and are therefore more likely to feel isolated and to become clinically depressed (Coyne and Downey, 1991) or suicidal. This may lead recently widowed men to neglect themselves – for example, by failing to eat properly – thus compromising their immune systems and putting themselves at risk of cardiovascular disease and other health problems.

In more general terms, House, Landis and Umberson (1988) report that social isolation can lead to increased mortality in both humans and animals. Likewise, Kawachi and Kennedy (1997) claim that 'socially isolated people die at two or three times the rate of well connected people, presumably reflecting the former's limited access to sources of emotional support, instrumental support (for example, financial aid), and other forms of support' (p. 1038).

Social support and health-related behaviour

Researchers suggest that the effects of social support on health can be either direct or mediated by health-related behaviour (for example, Cohen, 1988). If an individual has a large social network, then they have more potential access to a wider range of information about the best ways in which to promote good health. As a result, they might be encouraged to make lifestyle changes, such as giving up smoking or reducing alcohol consumption, which in turn will lead to a reduced risk of disease. The argument that social support enhances self-esteem and feelings of self-worth (Wills 1985, cited in Ganster and Victor, 1988) – thus leading to less risk of depression and self-neglect – can also be applied to health behaviour.

In addition to giving the individual access to a wide range of information about health and helping him or her cope with periods of ill health (Jerrome, 1990), social integration also provides social controls and pressures which can influence their health-related behaviour. Schwarzer and Leppin (1992) point out that other people can exert an influence on an individual's health in a number of ways, not all of them benign or beneficial. Thus, social support can have either 'positive' or 'negative' effects. 'Negative' social support refers to the way in which the behaviour of family members or friends might encourage individuals to take up risky practices, such as smoking (Gottlieb and Baker, 1986; Wills and Vaughan, 1989), or undermine their attempts to make behavioural changes, such as reducing alcohol consumption. For example, McBride *et al.* (1998) found that pregnant women whose partners continue to smoke are less likely to give up smoking successfully than women whose partners are non-smokers, and Stanton and McGee (1996) found that 3 per cent of their sample were actively encouraging – or forcing – their peers to try smoking. 'Positive' social support refers to the way in which a spouse, friends or family members can enhance health by encouraging health-promoting behaviours (Umberson, 1992), for example, by joining in with attempts to lose weight or give up smoking (McBride *et al.*, 1998), and helping an individual to follow a special diet or take regular exercise.

Researchers (Gottlieb 1983, 1988) have written extensively about designing support interventions (in the work place, in specific communities or among peer groups) to encourage health-promoting behaviours, such as giving up smoking and practising 'safer sex'. However, the evidence suggests that health promotion campaigns might be far more effective if more were known about the relationship between stress, social support and health, and about the mechanisms whereby support encourages health-promoting behaviours. For example, it has been suggested that support may have a more positive effect on health or health behaviour, especially in times of stress, if it is provided by people of the same gender, age, ethnicity and socioeconomic background, or by people who have shared similar life-experiences (House, 1981; Cohen and McKay, 1984).

The 'costs' of social support

Thoits (1995) has found that the 'costs' of social support, for both supporter and recipient, can sometimes outweigh its benefits for health. Citing Rook (1992), she points out that some support attempts may harm the recipient rather than enhance wellbeing because supporters may be seen as 'interfering', or they may be well-meaning but inept. According to Coyne and Downey (1991), low perceived support might well indicate that an individual has very few potential supporters; alternatively, it could mean that he or she has several relationships but feels that they are unsatisfactory in some way. Even when an individual reports a high level of perceived support, received support may fall well short of expectations. For example, support may be given grudgingly, especially by a spouse or members of the immediate family, which does little to enhance the individual's self-esteem or feelings of self-worth, since it is provided out of a sense of obligation and duty rather than love or affection (Coyne and Downey, 1991; Thoits, 1992). Similarly, supporters might consider the individual to be incapable of doing anything for themselves, in which case the individual might feel overwhelmed by unwelcome support. Thoits (1995, citing Aneshensel, Pearlin and Roberleigh, 1993) points out that giving support out of a sense of duty or obligation can subject the supporter, as well as the receiver, to physical and psychological stress which might have adverse effects on his or her health. Some support relationships, for example, within family networks, are based on perceived obligations to care, or on perceived 'rights' to be cared for. Ginn, Arber and Cooper, 1997 (citing Crohan and Antonucci, 1989) point out that because they are based on reciprocity and mutual interests, 'friendships affirm identity and self-worth in a way that relationships with extended families may not' (p. 31).

3. Measures of social support

This section examines how social support is most commonly measured for research purposes. The limitations of certain of these measures are highlighted and discussed, notably the use of marital status.

Social networks and integration

In terms of both structure and function, researchers (House and Kahn, 1985; Vaux, 1988) have identified three separate components of social support – relational content, social network composition and social integration. The relational content of social support is measured in terms of satisfaction with the quality of support and the meaning it has for the individual; issues such as conflict and control may also be taken into account.

Berkman (1984) advocates that social network content should be measured in terms of the widest possible range of factors, including network density, homogeneity and gender composition. Social integration is measured in terms of whether or not an individual has any social relationships and, if he or she does, how often and with how many people they have contact (House, Landis and Umberson, 1988); the number of active social roles an individual has – for example, mother, friend, colleague, sibling – can also be used as a measure of their degree of social integration (Thoits, 1983). The most commonly used measures of social integration, especially in epidemiological studies, are marital status, frequency of contact with network members, and group affiliations, such as being a member of a church.

Significant others

The commonest measure of perceived support is whether or not an individual has a close, confiding relationship with a significant other. Having someone to confide in has been found to reduce the adverse health effects of stress (Cohen and Wills, 1985), as does believing that love and esteem are available from a significant other, such as a spouse or partner (Sarason, Pierce and Sarason, 1990). However, the use of marital relationships as a measure of social support can be called into question, because 'being married/in a partnership' does not give any indication of network size, or of levels of perceived or received support. Nor does being married necessarily mean that an individual either gives or receives support or can expect to receive support from his or her partner in times of crisis; indeed, Waring (1985, cited by Madge and Marmot, 1987) argues that whether or not a marital relationship has positive health benefits depends on the extent to which each partner feels that their support of the other is reciprocated.

Nevertheless, a number of researchers have found that married people report higher levels of perceived support than single people (for example, Ross and Mirowsky, 1989; Turner and Marino, 1994), and Kulik and Mahler (1989) found that received support from a spouse has a beneficial effect on health. They measured levels of spouse support by counting the number of times men who were recovering from heart surgery were visited by their wives, and they found that men who received high levels of support from their wives using this measure made a more speedy recovery and were released from hospital an average of 1.26 days earlier than men who received lower levels of support.

Issues of personal agency and meaning

Much of the research into social support has been based on rather sweeping assumptions, for example, that all marital relationships are close, confiding and mutually supportive;

that everyone *wants* to be involved in intense supportive relationships, such as marriage or close friendship; that the more friends an individual has, the more support is available to them; that all types of stress are potentially harmful to health; and that social relationships generally have benign or beneficial effects (Madge and Marmot, 1987; Schwarzer and Leppin, 1992; Thoits, 1995). In social support research, too little attention has been paid to the personal meanings which events and relationships have for individuals (Madge and Marmot, 1987; Thoits, 1994). For example, some marital relationships are characterised by conflict rather than mutual support and affection (Coyne and Downey, 1991) and, in consequence, both partners may be subject to chronic stress. In such circumstances the acute stress of divorce can have positive effects on psychological wellbeing; indeed, Thoits (1995) argues that supposedly stressful events, such as divorce, are sometimes 'problem-solving acts' engineered by the individual 'to solve otherwise intractable problems' (p. 58). In addition, Reissman (1990) and Silver, Boon and Stones (1983) (both cited by Thoits, 1995) have found that, after a period of adjustment to their new circumstances (during which there may indeed be health problems, such as depression), some people are able to attach a very positive meaning to the experience of divorce; women are likely to report that they feel more self-confident and in control of their lives, and men are likely to feel better able to communicate their feelings to others.

Problems with measuring social support

As in stress research, measures of social support and health vary from study to study, which makes it difficult to compare results and evaluate studies. This is an area in which more qualitative research might be useful, since the consensus amongst commentators is that the most widely used measures of social integration and/or perceived social support may not be capturing these phenomena with any statistically useful degree of accuracy. Once again, using marital status as an example, all this measure indicates is the presence in an individual's life of one person who might – or might not – be a source of support. As Coyne and Downey (1991) point out, being in a happy, supportive marital relationship can indeed reduce the risk of clinical depression but 'this positive effect is dwarfed by the negative one of being married and unable to talk to one's spouse' (p. 412). They go on to argue that researchers may be looking at social support from the wrong end of the telescope, because 'the apparent benefits of having support may in large part represent freedom from the deleterious effects of relationships that are conflictual, insecure, or otherwise not sustaining' (Coyne and Downey, 1991, p. 413).

Being in a marital relationship could indicate the existence of a wide social network of children, family members and friends (Ginn, Arber and Cooper, 1997); however, these relationships might be a source of stress rather than support (Thoits, 1995), or might not be perceived as supportive by the individual. Being unmarried, widowed or divorced – especially in old age (Ginn, Arber and Cooper, 1997) – might well indicate that someone is socially isolated, has a very small social network and has no close functional relationships; however, many single people – especially those in younger age groups – have busy social lives, several close confiding relationships, and large diverse social networks. Single measures, such as 'marital status', cannot take account of age- or gender-related variations in network size and perceived support over time, nor of the meanings which events and circumstances have for the persons concerned.

Social capital

Uchino, Cacioppo and Kiecolt-Glaser (1996) argue that it is important to conceptualise social support as a multidimensional construct, and Madge and Marmot (1987, p. 93) suggest that 'the ideal study' of social integration and support would take account of factors such as variations in social support over time, and gender differences in perceived and received support. Some writers have used the term 'social capital' as a characteristic of individuals in order to measure their access to a variety of resources, including social support. For example, in his study of 'dropping out' of high school, Coleman (1988) applied the term 'social capital' to parent–child interaction within the family, as well as to parent-to-parent interaction within the community; Coleman's study is examined in more detail in Chapter 3.

More generally, however, the term 'social capital' is applied to those features of a community or society which promote cohesion and a sense of 'belonging', and which enable its members to co-operate for the benefit of all. Morgan (1986) argues that 'social capital resources inhere in the social ties of a network. These resources are recognized by individuals as information channels and general social support' (p. 39). Networks of communication and mutual support which span age, class, gender and other social divides, and promote trust within and between groups, are important features of the types of social relationship which generate high levels of social capital (Hogan, 1998). Social capital – as a characteristic of communities rather than individuals – is the focus of Chapter 3.

2. Social capital and the health of the community

Recent studies, for example, by Diehr *et al.* (1993), Ellaway and McIntyre (1996) and Evans *et al.* (1989) have investigated the health and health behaviours of people living in different types of community environment. Evans *et al.* (1989) found that living in overcrowded circumstances can lead people to withdraw from social contact, thus leading to a breakdown in socially supportive relationships and adverse consequences for health; Diehr *et al.* (1993) found significant differences between the communities they examined in terms of smoking, consumption of alcohol and fat, and using seat-belts. They conclude that the environment has an effect on health-related behaviours, and suggest that changing the community environment is one way in which it might be possible to change individual health behaviours. Likewise, Gabbay (1988) suggests that researchers and policymakers need to address 'not just the causes of disease but the causes of the causes: poverty, inequalities, social exclusion, unemployment, and all the other features of the physical and social environment that converge to undermine health' (p. 1). Kawachi and Kennedy (1997) point out that, because research has tended to focus on health-related social resources – such as social support – that derive from social network interaction at the individual level, 'the social context in which people live their lives' has been neglected. Thus, researchers have ignored the possibility 'that entire communities or societies might be lacking in social connections' (p. 1038).

A number of epidemiologists, including Kawachi, Kennedy and colleagues, have embarked on a programme of research using the concept of 'social capital' to investigate the links between health, mortality and the social resources that are available at the community and societal level. This chapter examines some of this research, and also looks at studies in areas unrelated to health which nonetheless provide useful insights into the way in which 'social connections' might be regenerated for the purposes of promoting good health for the whole community.

Putnam (1995) defines social capital as the 'features of social organisation such as networks, norms, and social trust that facilitate coordination and collaboration for mutual benefit' (p. 67). Coleman (1988) conceptualised social capital as deriving from interaction between the social, human and financial resources available to an individual or community. Various criteria have been used by Coleman (1988), Putnam (1995) and others to measure levels of social capital. Thus, the 'stocks' of social capital which are available at the collective level may include any or all of the following elements:

- *Social resources,* such as informal reciprocal or altruistic support arrangements between neighbours or colleagues, or within and between friendship networks, neighbourhoods and specific 'communities'. Community is defined as groups of people who share a collective sense of identity and purpose as a result of having a common personal characteristic, belief or interest, such as locality, lifestyle, disability, occupation, religious faith, age, ethnicity, sexuality or social class.
- *The collective resources* of a neighbourhood or community, notably the level of civic activity, including tenants' associations, food co-operatives, volunteer co-ordination schemes, 'Neighbourhood Watch' schemes and credit unions; the level of trust and communication between neighbours and community members; the degree of collective trust in institutions such as the police and government bodies; levels of fear of crime; feelings of 'belonging' and social cohesion; access to sources of welfare provision.
- *Economic resources*, including levels of unemployment in an area or within a particular community; the quality of the environment, including housing and amenities; the level of local crime.
- *Cultural resources,* such as the perceived quality of local schools, libraries, meeting places and performance venues.

1. Coleman, Putnam and social capital

James S. Coleman (1988; also, Bourdieu, 1986) was among the first to bring the term 'social capital' to widespread attention. Robert Putnam has expanded on many of Coleman's themes and has written more extensively and prolifically about 'social capital' than any other writer; consequently, in addition to his own extensive body of research and commentary, much of the social capital literature consists of critiques of Putnam's work in this field.

Social capital and co-operation

Putnam (1993) claims that, 'if properly measured' (p. 5), social capital can indicate the human resources to which the members of a community have access. He suggests that the higher the level of human resources available in the community – measured in terms of social capital – the easier it is for people to work together for the common good. The more people work together, the more social capital is produced; however, the less people work co-operatively together, the more the community's 'stocks' of social capital will be depleted, and the harder it will be for them to work effectively together in the future. Social capital is therefore a 'moral resource', supplies of which increase with use, unlike physical capital – such as food or cash – supplies of which are depleted with use. Like financial capital, however, 'social capital is productive, making possible the achievement of certain ends that in its absence would not be possible' (Coleman, 1988, p. S98). Furthermore, social capital is a 'public good', like fresh air, that is not the private property of any of those who benefit from it and cannot be marketed like other commodities.

Putnam (1993) argues that there has been a decline in recent years of co-operative actions for mutual benefit. All the members of a community would undoubtedly benefit if they were to co-operate but, as 'games theory' has demonstrated, people tend to weigh up the personal costs and benefits of taking any action. Putnam (1993, 1996) argues that more and more people are deciding that they will not join in with promoting a cause which, if it succeeded, would directly enhance their own wellbeing, because, if the cause fails, they will have wasted valuable time and effort, and will be no better off. If they do not expend any of their own resources they will not be any worse off if the cause fails, and if it succeeds through other people's efforts they will be better off anyway.

Networks, norms and trust

It is this type of logic which was found to be prevalent in the most unsuccessful of the newly-established Italian regional governments studied by Putnam, Leonardi and Nanetti (1993). They expected to find that certain 'obvious' factors would explain a regional government's success or failure, for example, its political affiliations or ideology, the levels of poverty or affluence in the region, and the degree of stability or mobility within its population. The wealthiest regions had the most successful governments; however, Putnam, Leonardi and Nanetti (1993) concluded that the regions were not successful because they were rich, but were rich because they were civic-minded. That is, they found that the best predictor of success or failure was whether or not the region had 'strong traditions of civic engagement – voter turnout, newspaper readership, membership of choral societies and literary circles, Lions clubs, and soccer clubs' (p. 2).

Putnam, Leonardi and Nanetti (1993) found the most unsuccessful governments, such as that of Sicily, to be 'inefficient, lethargic and corrupt' (p. 2), and the regions they governed to be 'uncivic', that is, characterised by lack of a sense of citizenship and civic responsibility, and fear of crime. Although people living in these areas demanded more severe penalties, there was a tendency to believe that laws were meant to be broken and that crime was an issue for the 'bosses' to deal with rather than the citizens; on the whole, the people felt 'powerless, exploited and unhappy'. In comparison, they found that the most successful governments, such as that of Tuscany, were characterised by innovation and initiative; their leaders were honest and cared about such issues as equal opportunities for all; they had introduced, for example, job-training and investment programmes, and projects to improve health facilities and environmental standards. Putnam, Leonardi and Nanetti found the more successful regions to be affluent, dynamic and democratic 'civic communities' (p.2), characterised by high levels of trust between citizens; the norms in such regions were that people would abide by the region's laws and be fair in their dealings with each other and, on the whole, the citizens valued 'solidarity, civic participation and integrity'.

Generating social capital

Putnam (1993) argues that the more successful of the Italian regional governments serve as role-models for those engaged in trying to solve major social problems elsewhere in the world. Their success demonstrates that dynamic civic networks both generate, and are themselves generated, by co-ordinated effort. Furthermore, such networks allow for the communication of information, for example, about the trustworthiness, or otherwise, of particular groups or persons; Coleman (1998, citing Merry, 1984) claims that gossip among network members acts as a form of 'collective sanction' (p. S106) and helps to prevent crime and other deviant behaviours.

The successful regional governments also show how participation in one area of social life can increase levels of social capital in completely unrelated areas (Coleman, 1988; Putnam, 1993; Putnam, Leonardi and Nanetti, 1993). Putnam (1993) uses the example of Tuscan choral societies in which people participate simply because they enjoy singing; nevertheless, their participation serves to enhance the community's overall stocks of social capital, including the social trust which helps to reduce the incidence of crime. If social capital consists of ties of norms and trust that can be generated by belonging to a small local club but which potentially benefit the whole society, it therefore follows that investment made in one area of social capital can increase stocks in many other areas (Putnam, 1993). For example, investment in education and training alone might have the potential to improve communication skills, enhance self-confidence, improve job prospects and enable people to move into employment and out of poverty, which in turn could boost the individual, local, regional and national economy and give people access to better housing, better nutrition and better health.

Putnam (1993) argues that social capital can affect economic growth more directly by fostering 'sturdy norms of generalized reciprocity: I'll do this for you now, in the expectation that down the road you or someone else will return the favor' (p. 3). An example of social capital working in this way is the 'networking' through which deals are struck and information is exchanged in the business community. Business people may also be linked by relationships that exist outside the single context of work, for example, they may share the same background, educational experience, hobby or religion, with such 'multiplex' relationships allowing 'the resources of one relationship to be appropriated for use in others' (Coleman, 1988, p. S109). Coleman (1988) and Putnam (1993) discuss the very close-knit diamond-broking community in NewYork in which levels of mutual trust are so high that dealers allow customers to take gemstones worth many thousands of pounds to their own offices for closer examination and assessment. In such cases, successful collaboration with little or no abuse of trust encourages further collaboration in the future; sanctions – such as ostracism and withdrawal of privileges – also prevent abuse of trust.

However, close-knit networks can be very exclusive and may not extend across class, gender or ethnic boundaries. Coleman (1988) points out that 'the wholesale diamond market in New York City . . . is Jewish, with a high degree of intermarriage, living in the same community in Brooklyn, and going to the same synagogues' (p. S99). He argues that, like many other specialist business communities, 'it is essentially a closed community' (p. S99); therefore some people may be excluded from enjoying the benefits of sharing, for example, the type of information which would help them find a job (Coleman, 1988; Portes and Landolt, 1996). Putnam (1993) and Kawachi and Kennedy (1997) note that members of Afro-American and other ethnic groups living in run-down inner-city areas are often excluded in this way. Putnam reports that, in consequence, churches in some areas have begun to 'network' on behalf of members of their congregation or the local community in general. By using their own network contacts and by pledging their own stocks of social capital as 'collateral' – notably, their good reputations for trustworthiness and honesty – churches vouch for people who do not have a good reputation of their own, for example, individuals with criminal records or former drug-addicts, when they try to obtain loans or look for work. The churches put their trust in people not to let them down, and, for the individuals concerned, having so much trust placed in them can give a tremendous boost to their self-esteem and morale.

Putnam (1993) argues that this type of large-scale social support can enhance social capital for the whole community, and that policymakers should take note of initiatives which successfully generate social capital when they plan interventions to tackle problems, such as deteriorating standards of education in schools. Coleman (1988) found that it is not the superior abilities of students which make some schools more successful educators of children, but the high levels of social capital generated by parental interest and involvement in the educational process. Coleman uses the example of a district school in the USA where Asian parents were observed to buy two copies of every textbook, one for their child and one for the mother, who, regardless of her own level of educational attainment, would follow the syllabus in order to be able to help her child do well in his or her lessons. Putnam (1993) believes that parental choice schemes represent flawed logic, because allowing choice in the public sector leads parents who are interested and involved in their children's education to opt for schools with 'a good reputation', which is a form of social capital. This leaves so-called 'sink schools' to cater for pupils whose parents are less likely to contribute to generating or re-generating these schools' dwindling stocks of social capital.

Kawachi and Kennedy (1997) point out that success in adult life may be influenced by the number of 'network contacts' made during education and in the neighbourhood. Thus, people who live in depressed and run-down areas and attend 'sink schools' are unlikely to establish these types of mutually beneficial social relationships. Kawachi and Kennedy (1997) argue, therefore, that 'concepts like . . . social capital are inherently "ecological", that is, they are characteristics of places, not individuals' (p. 1039). People who possess more social and cultural resources in the form of education and initiative are more likely to be successful in employment and to move away from inner-city areas to the affluent suburbs. This outward migration effectively deprives a decaying community of the very people who are likely to have the drive and energy to initiate the regeneration of social capital (Putnam, 1993).

2. Measuring social capital

The concept of 'social capital' includes the following types of resources available to a community or locality:

- social resources, such as formal and informal support networks
- collective resources, including social trust
- economic resources, such as levels of unemployment
- cultural resources, such educational facilities.

The majority of researchers accept Putnam's definition of social capital, that is, the 'features of social organization, such as networks, norms, and social trust that facilitate coordination and cooperation for mutual benefit' (1995, p. 67). Thus, researchers who use data from national or international social surveys tend to measure social capital in terms of levels of social trust and group affiliation (Putnam, 1996; Kennedy, Kawachi and Prothrow-Stith, 1996). Questions covering these issues are included in most US large-scale surveys, such as the General Social Survey (GSS); Putnam (1996) used data from this survey to support his hypothesis that levels of social capital are declining in contemporary American society. However, these measures are not available in most UK national social surveys.

Other researchers have collected qualitative and quantitative data in smaller-scale local studies; for example, Flora (1995) investigated the relationship between sustainable agriculture and social capital in rural communities, and measured social capital in terms of 'community effectiveness'. In their study of the relationship between social capital and violence in an urban setting, Sampson, Raudenbush and Earls (1997) used a similar expression – 'community efficacy' – which they measured in terms of levels of trust and social integration; they found that the higher the level of community efficacy, the lower the level of violence.

Social capital and educational attainment

Coleman (1988) investigated the relationship between educational achievement and levels of social capital in the family and surrounding adult community, using graduation from high school, or 'dropping out' beforehand, as measures of educational achievement. He argues that any analysis which examines the effects of social capital should take account of the interaction between 'human capital' (that is, personal and cultural resources) and 'social capital' (that is, social and economic resources) (S110). He therefore conceptualised 'social capital' not only as a characteristic of the individual, and of his or her family, which could be measured using social surveys, but also as a characteristic of the community in which they live. He used the following measures of personal and family resources:

- socioeconomic status: 'a single variable constructed of parents' education, parents' income, father's occupational status, and household possessions' (p. S111)
- ethnicity
- number of siblings
- number of residential moves (and thus changes of school)
- whether or not the mother worked before her children started school
- the mother's expectations of her children's level of educational attainment
- level of communication between children and parents about personal matters
- whether or not both parents were present in the household.

Coleman (1988) used the following measures of social capital in the surrounding adult community:

- 'the social relationships that exist among parents' (p. S113), notably, exchanges of information and levels of trust
- norms of acceptable behaviour, and sanctions

- affiliation with local organisations.

He found that access to social capital both within the family and in the surrounding adult community had 'considerable value in reducing the probability of dropping out of high school' (p. S119). For example, Roman Catholic and other denominational schools had significantly lower drop-out rates than non-denominational independent and public sector schools. Coleman claims that this difference resulted from the higher levels of social capital available to *all* pupils (even when stocks of social capital were low within some individuals' families) as a result of their parents sharing the same religious affiliation and norms of acceptable behaviour – and, in all probability, living in the same area, belonging to the same clubs and talking amongst themselves about the progress and behaviour of their own and other people's children.

Social capital and child development

More recently, Runyan *et al.* (1998) have investigated the relationship between social capital and the wellbeing of 600 pre-school children taking part in a longitudinal study of neglect and child-abuse. They measured social capital in terms of the characteristics of the child's family; thus, each child's social capital was measured by awarding one point for each of the following:

- having two or more parents or adult carers in the home
- social support being available for the mother or female carer
- having no more than one sibling
- neighbourhood support being available for the family
- regular church attendance.

Measuring each child's progress using standard developmental tests, Runyan *et al.* (1998) found that only 13 per cent were 'doing well'; however, having the benefit of only one of the indicators of social capital increased the chances of 'doing well' by 29 per cent, and having the benefit of any three of the indicators increased the chance of thriving by 66 per cent. The sum of all the indicators – rather than any one single indicator – was most strongly associated with a child's wellbeing. However, the three individual elements of social capital which best enhanced the chance of a child thriving were found to be church membership, the level of the female carer's perceived support and the availability of neighbourhood support; Runyan *et al.* (1998) found church affiliation to be particularly important because it involved both child and parent in the same social network.

Social capital in agricultural communities

Flora (1995) identified a number of indicators of enhanced social cohesion and increased collective endeavour during her study of rural communities in the Great Plains and Corn Belt areas of the USA. In his review of Flora's study of sustainable agriculture, Campbell (1995) reports that she compared two communities where 'sustainable' agricultural practices had been introduced (for example, reducing or eliminating the use of chemical fertilisers, insecticides and weed killers) with two communities where 'conventional' farming methods still prevailed. The aim of Flora's study was to investigate whether or not sustainable agriculture enhanced the levels of social capital available to the surrounding community. She measured social capital in terms of the community's 'effectiveness', which she defined as its ability to identify problems and find appropriate solutions.

Campbell (1995) reports that levels of cohesion and effectiveness remained roughly the same in the two 'conventional' farming communities over the five-year study period, whereas the two 'sustainable' communities 'experienced significant increases in their ability to mobilize community resources' (Campbell, 1995, p. 2). Flora (1995) identified a number of indicators of enhanced social capital. These ranged from increased debate between local residents, focusing on the pros and cons of sustainable agriculture, to the introduction of a state-backed community development plan; the setting up of small local companies to cater for the needs of sustainable farmers; and increased participation in local organisations and politics. Flora (1995) suggests that the mechanism whereby sustainable agriculture might enhance social capital is the introduction into the community of 'the problem-solving mindset that is integral to sustainable farming, the ability to adapt to local conditions while striving towards economic, environmental and social goals' (cited in Campbell, 1995, p. 3).

Social capital and health promotion

A number of researchers (for example, Daly, 1997; Kreuter, Lezin and Baker, 1998) are interested in the concept of social capital as a means of investigating the failure of community health programmes. Kreuter and colleagues claim that 'there is evidence to suggest that at least some portion of so-called "program-failures" is likely to be attributable to pre-existing social factors, one of which may be manifested by low levels of social capital' (1998, p. 1). In a future comparative study Kreuter and colleagues intend to measure four components of social capital – trust, civic participation, social engagement and reciprocity – in communities which have been estimated (by residents and community leaders) to have high and low levels of social capital. The aim of their study is 'to create a community-level measure of social capital' that is 'at once practical and valid' (1998, p. 2). Kreuter, Lezin and Baker point out that although Kawachi,

Kennedy and colleagues (Kennedy, Kawachi and Prothrow-Stith, 1996; Kawachi and Kennedy, 1997) and Wilkinson (1992, 1996) have recently highlighted the link between social, political and economic factors and health, funding for community-based health promotion remains 'tied to a specific health category' (Kreuter, Lezin and Baker, 1998, p. 3), such as HIV/AIDS or coronary heart disease. Kreuter, Lezin and Baker therefore believe that it is essential to find an effective means of measuring social capital in order to persuade fund-holders to include an inventory of local social capital when planning community-based prevention programmes; in this way, 'funders would be able to make more informed decisions about the most productive ways to contribute infusions of health-related funding to a given community – either to bolster the capacity that is requisite for successful interventions, or move directly to the interventions themselves' (1998:3).

Other research has focused on investigating the ways in which social capital might be built or regenerated and used as a resource in the promotion of health. Gillies (1997) reviewed a large number of health promotion initiatives world-wide for the World Health Organization and the Health Education Authority. She found that the most successful of these focused on the health needs of the community rather than on individual health-related behaviour. Successful initiatives utilised and generated social capital by exploiting existing alliances and partnerships at the local, regional and national level, and linking members of the lay, medical, academic and business communities. Gillies believes that understanding the underlying mechanisms of 'networking' is essential in situations where social capital needs to be built 'from scratch'. She found that models of 'best practice' were flexible enough to adapt to sudden changes in local, regional and national circumstances, and clearly demonstrated how individuals and groups 'networked' with each other to exchange information and collaborate in health promotion activities.

Hyden (1998) also believes that models of 'best practice' – either their own or those of other groups – encourage people to engage in collective action. However, Hyden points out that unsuccessful efforts to generate social capital, especially where people lose trust in each other, can ruin future attempts, since 'trust, once destroyed, is difficult to re-build' (p. 29). Putnam's research (1993, 1996) into declining levels of trust in contemporary America is examined in the next section.

3. Measuring the correlates of levels of social capital

Putnam (1993, 1996) claims that, since the end of World War II, there has been a steady decline in levels of social trust, measured in social surveys in the USA by individuals' responses to this type of statement: 'Most people can be trusted – or would most people try to take advantage of you if they could?' (National Opinions Research Centre surveys, 1986–90, cited in Kawachi and Kennedy, 1997). Putnam (1993, 1996) argues that there has been a decline in individual levels of social trust, together with a corresponding decline in group affiliation, which indicates an overall decline in social capital throughout the USA since the end of the 1940s. In a lengthy and detailed article entitled 'The strange disappearance of civic America', Putnam (1996) explains how, using data from the yearly US General Social Survey (GSS), he came to this conclusion. His arguments are summarised as follows:

Education

A high level of educational achievement is strongly correlated with increased civic engagement. Putnam (1996) suggests that this is because better-educated people generally have more money and 'skills, resources and inclinations that were imparted to them at home and in school' (p. 4). Therefore, civic engagement should have increased as educational levels rose during the post-war years, yet participation has declined during the past 25 years regardless of levels of educational achievement. Putnam argues that education remains such an important correlate of participation that it must be taken into account when exploring other potential correlates of civic engagement.

Mobility and locality

US census data show that levels of residential mobility have remained almost constant for the past 50 years; Putnam therefore argues that the decline in participation during this period cannot be explained by mobility and the difficulty of putting down 'roots' in a new community. The types of community organisation used to measure group affiliation vary considerably from area to area, but Putnam found that levels of trust and participation are, overall, a little higher in rural areas, small towns and the suburbs than in inner-city areas. Despite these small differences, there is a very similar level of decline in trust and participation in all parts of the USA; nevertheless, Putnam maintains that 'where we live and how long we've lived there matter for social capital' (p. 5).

Time

There is no evidence to suggest that the decline in community participation can be accounted for by what Putnam terms 'busy-ness' (as measured by time-budget studies). He found that employed people tend to belong to more groups than people outside the workforce, but that female part-time workers tend to have higher levels of trust and participation than female full-time workers and women who do not work. In general, however, Putnam found that working longer hours is associated with higher levels of participation, and he therefore concludes that 'if people are dropping out of community life, long hours do not seem to be the reason' (Putnam, 1996, p. 6).

Income

Holding education constant, people on low incomes, and those who feel financially insecure, tend to participate less and to be less trusting than people with higher levels of income. However, there has been a reduction in trust and participation across all levels of income, with a slightly higher level of decline among the affluent rather than low or middle-income groups. Putnam therefore concludes that 'poverty and economic inequality are dreadful, growing problems for America, but they are not the villains of *this* piece' (1996, p. 6).

Gender

Putnam found that women belong to slightly fewer voluntary groups than men but devote more time to them, and that women spend more time socialising informally. Controlling for education, relative declines in organisational membership and involvement are a little higher for women, but absolute declines are much the same for women and men.

Women and work

The increased movement of women into the workforce during the past 50 years is associated with the decline in both trust and participation; however, the association is far weaker than Putnam expected it to be. Non-working women belong to different types of organisations (for example, school-related groups) than working women (for example, professional associations); working women tend to belong to more voluntary groups, and to devote more time to organisational involvement overall, than non-working women. The decline in trust and participation has increased more rapidly for non-working than for working women, and time-budget data indicate that a 'major decline in informal socialising since 1965 has also been concentrated among housewives' (Putnam, 1996, p. 7). Community involvement is therefore rising slightly among working women and declining among non-working women. Putnam suggests that, in the past, women with initiative and organising skills had no choice but to devote their energies to community activities; these are now the types of women who are most likely to enter the workforce, 'thus lowering the average level of civic engagement among the remaining homemakers and raising the average among women in the workplace' (1996, p. 7).

Marriage, divorce and the family

'Successful marriage' (Putnam, 1996, p. 8) is associated with higher levels of trust and civic involvement, especially when there are children in the family. Controlling for education, age, ethnicity 'and so on' (p. 8), Putnam found that single men and women are significantly less likely to be trusting, or to participate, than those who are married or widowed. There is some evidence to suggest that 'loosening of family bonds' is associated with the decline in civic participation, partly because 'the family is, by some accounts, a key form of social capital' (p. 8). In the USA there has been an increase in the rate of divorce, notably during the 1960s and 1970s; an increase in the number of one-parent families; a doubling of single-person households since 1950; and a steep rise in the proportion of adults who are 'currently unmarried' (Putnam, p. 8). A reduction in the number of 'successful marriages' seems to be associated with a decline in levels of trust and participation, but may be mediated through a number of other factors; for example, Putnam suggests that among divorced people it might be reduced levels of income that are associated with less trust and participation.

Government policy

Some government policies, such as 'slum clearance schemes', can undermine social capital by severing local community ties, whereas others, such as the Head Start social and educational programme in the USA, can help to enhance trust and increase stocks of social capital. Putnam found no evidence in the GSS data to suggest that the extent of a state's welfare involvement or its level of welfare spending are associated with levels of social trust or participation. However, using data from the 1990–1 World Values Survey, Putnam found a positive correlation between social capital and state involvement in welfare provision, but he points out that 'this simple bivariate analysis, of course, cannot tell us whether social connectedness encourages welfare spending, whether the welfare state fosters civic engagement, or whether both are the result of some other unmeasured factor(s)' (1996, p. 9).

Ethnicity and racism

In response to claims that the level of civic engagement of white Americans has declined more rapidly since racial desegregation in the 1960s, Putnam argues that levels of social capital – measured in terms of both participation and trust – have declined equally rapidly among all ethnic groups during the same period. Furthermore, the decline in participation has been no more rapid among 'avowedly racist or segregationist whites' than among 'more tolerant whites' (Putnam, 1996, p. 9).

Age and cohort

Putnam found that age, like education, is a major predictor of civic engagement and trust. In comparison with younger people, he found that older Americans – until they reach their late 80s – tend to be more gregarious and to belong to more organisations, and are more likely to read newspapers and to vote. Putnam found that until the mid-1970s people tended to participate more and to become more trusting as they grew older. However, although older people's levels of participation and trust continue to be higher than those of younger people, successive cohorts since the 1970s have become less trusting, and have been less likely to participate in community activities, as they have become older. Putnam argues that this decline results from the gradual demise over the past 20 years of what he calls 'the long civic generation' (1996, p. 11) of people who reached adulthood before the 1950s. For example, controlling for education he found that, in comparison with people born in the 1960s, people born in the 1920s belong to nearly twice as many community organisations, are twice as likely to trust other people, are twice as likely to vote, and read newspapers three times as often. Putnam claims that 'each generation that reached adulthood since the 1940s has been less engaged in community affairs than its predecessor' (1996, p. 12); however, the effects of this reduction were masked by increased levels of educational achievement, and became apparent only when the cohorts born from the late 1940s onwards began to reach adulthood during the 1960s.

Television and technology

Having examined all the most likely causes of the decline in social capital – measured in terms of civic engagement and social trust – Putnam concludes that the 'prime suspect' (1996, p. 13) is television. Television became increasingly popular from the late 1940s onwards, the point at which the last of 'the long civic generation' reached adulthood and the first of the more socially disconnected cohorts was born. Watching television now accounts for 40 per cent of Americans' leisure-time and, controlling for education, income, age, ethnicity, locality and employment, is strongly and negatively correlated with social trust, group affiliation and community involvement. Putnam suggests that new forms of communications technology might foster increased levels of 'couch-potato behaviour' (1996, p. 15), leading to an even more rapid decrease in levels of civic engagement.

Critiques of Putnam's thesis

Schudson (1996) questions Putnam's criteria for measuring the decline in participation, such as membership of a club or political party. He argues that between 1967 and 1987, participation in the USA rose rather than fell, for example, that 'participation in a community problem-solving organisation' rose from 31 per cent in 1967 to 34 per cent in 1987 and 'working with others on a local problem' rose from 30 per cent to 34 per cent during the same period (1996, p. 1). Schudson argues that 'Putnam's measures may, in fact, overlook several types of civic activity' (1996, p. 1), such as occasional involvement in so-called 'single issue' civic activity, for example, to oppose a road-building scheme or the export of live animals. In addition, belonging to several clubs or groups does not mean that an individual is more 'civic-minded' than someone who belongs to only one organisation, such as a church. Multiple group membership gives no indication of an individual's degree of commitment, nor does belonging to just one organisation indicate the many civic activities that might be involved, such as being a volunteer driver, raising funds, and liaising with other community groups in the area. Furthermore, Skocpol (1996) notes that the US General Social Survey (GSS) – Putnam's principal source of data – asks about the 'types' of organisations to which respondents belong, rather than asking for a list of group or community activities. Using this measure, the GSS data does indeed show a decline in membership of formally constituted organisations, such as bowling leagues, but does not take account of the thousands of people who regularly go bowling in informal groups of friends or neighbours.

Skocpol (1996) also believes that Putnam (1996) has underestimated the effect on social capital of women taking their leadership and organisational skills into the workplace. Skocpol claims that, although there has been an undoubted downturn in civic engagement since the 1960s, 'what has changed has less to do with TV watching than with shifting elite allegiances' (1996, p. 3). She argues that, in the past, middle-class women in particular were prime movers in local cross-class community organisations, and that many of them were married to local business leaders and professionals. These women and men viewed civic activity as a 'stepping stone' to positions of greater authority in the community and business world, but, according to Skocpol, 'their counterparts now do better if they work long hours and network with each other through extra-local professional or trade associations, while dealing with politics by sending checks to lobbying groups headquartered in Washington DC' (1996, p. 4). Skocpol (1996) also questions the 'Tocqueville romanticism' (1996, p. 4) which she believes underpins much of Putnam's argument, that is, the capacity – identified by the French writer Alexis de Tocqueville (1966) – of post-revolutionary American citizens to organise themselves to solve local problems without being directed by central or local government. Skocpol points out that right-wing politicians in the USA have seized on the notion that the ability to band together to 'get things done' still lies dormant in the American people, and have used it to support the argument that this type of social capital would spontaneously regenerate if welfare support were to be reduced or withdrawn altogether. Skocpol comments that it would be ironic

> 'if, after pulling out of locally rooted associations, the very business and professional elites who blazed the path towards local civic disengagement were now to turn around and successfully argue that the less privileged Americans they left behind are the ones who must repair the nation's social connectedness, by pulling themselves together from below without much help from government or their privileged fellow citizens.'
>
> (1996, p. 6).

4. Social capital, social inequality and health

Ichiro Kawachi, Bruce Kennedy and colleagues have recently carried out a number of studies investigating the relationship between economic inequality and health, and have suggested that economic inequality reduces social cohesion and integration, and increases social isolation. Kari *et al.* (1994), and others, have discussed the relationship between social capital and health-related social problems, and have suggested ways in which the concept of social capital might assist policymakers to address problems of health care and health promotion.

In a number of studies, social capital has been measured in terms of levels of civic trust and participation in community activities (for example, Putnam, Leonardi and Nanetti, 1993). Kawachi, Kennedy and colleagues have used measures of social capital to indicate the level of social cohesion in a community or society, which, they argue, has important implications for health: ' . . . that social cohesion enhances wellbeing is by now a well-established fact. Ever since Durkheim's study of the causes of suicide, numerous epidemiological studies have shown that people who are socially integrated live longer' (Kawachi and Kennedy, 1997, p. 1038). Kawachi, Kennedy and Lochner (1997) cite the study of Alameda County in California by Berkman and Syme (1979) in which it was found that regardless of 'risky' behaviours, such as smoking, drinking and taking too little exercise, the rates of mortality (from all causes) of people with few social relationships were between twice and three times as high as those for people with larger social networks.

Kawachi and Kennedy (1997) suggest that social cohesion is undermined by increased income inequality between rich and poor, which in turn causes hostility and mistrust. Kawachi, Kennedy and Lochner (1997) cite the example of Roseto, a small town in Pennsylvania, where many of the residents are descendants of migrants from the same Italian village. During the 1950s, the rate of heart attacks in Roseto was found to be in the region of 40 per cent lower than the local average, yet residents were no less likely to smoke, to take too little exercise or to be overweight than other Pennsylvanians. The only major difference between Roseto and other towns in the area was the 'social cohesiveness and ethos of egalitarianism that characterized the community' (1997, p. 1); all the residents of Roseto enjoyed a similar level of income and standard of living, and 'conspicuous consumption' was frowned upon (1997, p. 2). By 1965, however, younger people had sought work outside the community and levels of income had begun to vary from family to family; one or two people flaunted their wealth by buying expensive cars and taking exotic holidays, and other better-off families followed suit. As income inequalities within the community became visibly apparent, so the rate of heart attacks rose until, by the mid-1970s, it was the same as that of other nearby towns.

Using data from surveys conducted in the USA, Kennedy, Kawachi and Prothrow-Stith (1996) found a strong correlation between income inequality and overall mortality, and also deaths from heart disease, homicide and cancer. Kennedy and colleagues measured income inequality using the 'Robin Hood Index', which calculates the amount of redistribution of income from rich to poor that would be required to achieve equality of income; they found a correlation between income inequality and both social mistrust and levels of community participation (measured by membership of clubs, interest groups and church congregations). In addition, they found a strong correlation between mortality and high levels of social mistrust and low levels of community involvement.

Kawachi, Kennedy and Lochner (1997) argue that income inequality, when measured using the Robin Hood Index, leads to a reduction in levels of social capital, because 'the larger the income gap, the lower is citizens' trust in each other' (1997, p. 4), and the lower the levels of participation in community organisations. Furthermore, they argue that income inequality can explain differences in mortality between nations – for example, the USA has a very high standard of living yet has a lower life expectancy (76.1 years in 1993) than some poorer countries. The same authors suggest that this is because the distribution of wealth is less polarised in countries such as the Netherlands (77.5 years) and Spain (77.7 years), and they point out that the countries with the smallest gap between the incomes of rich and poor have the highest life expectancy, that is, Sweden (78.3 years) and Japan (79.6 years). Kawachi, Kennedy and Lochner (1997) and Wilkinson (1996) claim that although life expectancy has increased in recent years in the USA, it might have been higher and the increase more rapid had it not been for the effects on health of the widening gap between the incomes of rich and poor.

Kawachi and Kennedy argue that the relationship between income inequality and mortality seems to be 'mediated through the withering of social capital' (1997, p. 1039). A study by Kawachi, Kennedy and Lochner (1997) tests this hypothesis by investigating the relationship between social capital and public health using data from a survey conducted in 39 American states. Although Putnam (1996) found only small differences in levels of social capital from state to state, using alternative survey data, Kawachi, Kennedy and Lochner (1997) found that 'there are quite marked geographical variations in civic trust and association membership across the United States, and when these indicators of social capital are arrayed against regional differences in mortality and morbidity, the resulting correlations are striking' (1997, p. 2). They found that higher average mortality rates are associated with lower levels of social trust and with lower levels of membership of voluntary groups, and that there is a strong correlation between levels of social trust and measures of self-reported wellbeing. Because Putnam has repeatedly used 'bowling alone' as a metaphor for the decline in social capital, Kawachi and colleagues also investigated the relationship between league participation and health, and found that 'bowling league membership turns out to correlate rather well with who lives and dies' (1997, p. 4).

5. 'Health as a civic question'*

As Coleman (1988), Gillies (1997) and many others have pointed out, social capital is a resource that is generated by interaction among people and which enables them to collaborate for the benefit of all. The World Health Organization (WHO) defines health promotion as 'a key investment':

> 'Health promotion, through investment and action, has a marked impact on the determinants of health so as to create the greatest health gain for people, to contribute significantly to the reduction of inequalities in health, to further human rights, and to build social capital . . . Health promotion is carried out *by* and *with* people, not *on* or *to* people. It improves both the ability of individuals to take action, and the capacity of groups, organizations or communities to influence the determinants of health'.
>
> (Jakarta Declaration, WHO, 1997)

*Kari *et al.* (1994)

Thus, better standards of health can be promoted by collaborative efforts within the community (WHO, 1997; Kari *et al.*, 1994), and social capital enables 'the achievement of certain ends that in its absence would not be possible' (Coleman, 1988, p. S98).

As Gillies (1997) points out, health has hitherto been seen primarily as a characteristic of the individual, hence the emphasis in health promotion on making individual behavioural changes. However, the Jakarta Declaration (WHO, 1997) highlights 'the need to understand and address those factors which affect health, but which are beyond the control of individual influence on behaviours or experience' (Gillies, 1997, p. 4), such as education, income inequality, unemployment, housing and the quality of the local neighbourhood.

The role of the medical expert

Although it is increasingly recognised that there are broader determinants of health than individual behaviour (Gillies, 1997), Kari *et al.* (1994) argue that there needs to be a change in the relationship between health professionals and those who consult them if health is to become a truly collaborative endeavour. At present, this relationship – whatever form it takes – is underpinned by 'the notion that expert medical knowledge can somehow fix the consequences of unhealthy lifestyles no matter what choices we make and rescue us from the pain and fear of death' (Kari *et al.*, 1994, p. 1). Furthermore, the same authors argue that health has increasingly come to be regarded as a commodity which can be bought and sold rather than as a 'public good'.

In the past, a paternalistic expert/patient relationship predominated (Kari *et al.*, 1994) in which patients were expected to do whatever they were told would benefit their health, without questioning the wisdom and authority of the medical profession. In this type of relationship, the patient takes on the 'sick role' (Parsons, 1975) and relinquishes control over his or her health. However, the 'sick role' has certain advantages for the patient; on the grounds of ill health, the individual can avoid onerous social responsibilities, and is freed from taking responsibility for his or her own state of health. In recent years, the expert/patient relationship has been replaced by a more commercial expert/customer relationship characterised by 'patient empowerment', which amounts to little more than allowing people a limited amount of choice between approved providers of specific services. Clients of the health services believe that they have a 'right to choose', yet even those with private medical insurance can be disadvantaged if there are no ethnic surgeons or dentists on the list of approved practitioners, or if the treatment they want or need is excluded from their policy (Kari *et al.*, 1994). Clients believe themselves to be 'empowered', but 'the tendency to 'professionalise' local networks often disempowers the very people who seek to take action and gain influence over determinants of health' (Coronary Prevention Group, 1997, p. 2).

'Templates' of success

Gillies (1997) and others have found that there are many health promotion initiatives world-wide which can serve as models of best practice and 'templates' (Putnam, 1995, p. 67) of success. For example, Kari *et al.* (1994) discuss several American initiatives which aim to develop collaborative relationships between health advisers and their clients, and to encourage civic activity as a means of promoting good health. This type of initiative is underpinned by the notion that individual choices can have community-wide effects, and by the notion that health professionals are citizens themselves and need to interact with other citizens in order to raise standards of health and health care for the whole community. Kari *et al.* cite the Oregon Health Reform Plan, which was seen as a controversial exercise because it allowed ordinary citizens to participate in determining Oregon's 'core health values' and in deciding how the state's health-care services should be managed. Instead of a committee of policymakers and medical professionals deciding, on their behalf, how the state's limited health resources should be allocated, lay people were invited to give their opinions and to discuss the issues involved. In some cases, lay notions of priority medical treatments differed from those of medical professionals. For example, in comparison with physicians and surgeons lay people gave cosmetic surgery a far higher priority, but public opinion prevailed on this issue and the plan was voted in by the US senate; the states of Georgia and California have recently initiated similar public consultation projects.

Another example cited by Kari *et al.* (1994) is 'Hospice Austin' (Texas) which increased ethnic group involvement in the hospice movement by raising funds to sponsor nursing scholarships; student nurses work part-time in their own communities while in training, and give a commitment to work for the hospice movement for at least two years after graduation. In addition, 'Hospice Austin' increased ethnic group volunteers by asking local church leaders to speak to their congregations about the movement. Ethnic minority volunteers and nurses have, in turn, been able to assist the hospice movement to tailor its services to the needs and beliefs of specific communities. In this way, for example, hospice workers learned that assisting with the care of a terminally ill member of an Hispanic family can be difficult or impossible without the full co-operation of the male head of the household. As in the case of social support at the individual level, there is evidence to suggest that interventions are more likely to be successful if support comes from people who have shared the same – or very similar – life experiences, or are members of the same community. Cox (1997) argues that in health promotion projects, for example, 'it is much harder to convince a population to take on healthier lifestyles if the messages come from people they do not trust' (p. 4).

'Templates' of success need not be related directly to health (Gillies, 1997; Kari *et al.*, 1994; Putnam, 1993, 1995, p. 67); they can be found in activities as diverse as animal rights protests, parent–teacher associations, parish councils, campaigns to protect the environment, sports teams, irrigation projects in the developing world and chess clubs in the former Soviet Union. Any type of project in which it can be shown that social capital has been simultaneously exploited and generated by means of forming alliances and partnerships, and from which clear benefits for the whole community – and not just a few 'insiders' – have resulted, will serve as a model. Where levels of social capital were low before the project began – as in the case of 'Hospice Austin' – successful collaborations demonstrate how community interest and action were mobilised and sustained. Kari *et al.* (1994) also point out that when social capital is successfully generated through health-related projects, this can extend outwards into the wider community, not only as improved standards of general health but also as networks of communication which can be used to address other social problems.

4. Conclusions

The research examined in Chapter 2 highlights the importance of social integration and social support for the health and wellbeing of the individual. Friends, family members and health professionals can provide support in a number of ways, for example, by providing care, and practical and emotional support in times of stress and illness, and by relieving social isolation and loneliness. Furthermore, although both 'negative' influences and lack of social support can undermine an individual's attempts to make health-related behavioural changes, such as giving up smoking, 'positive' social support can enhance his or her chances of success. Nevertheless, Gillies (1996, 1997) found that only one in four individuals successfully change their health-related behaviour, and they tend to be people who are 'better off, better motivated and better educated' (1997, p. 4). Thus, individuals' stocks of social capital – that is, the social, personal, economic and cultural resources to which they have access – can exert a considerable influence over their health experience. Furthermore, the opportunities which individuals have to accumulate social capital tend to be closely related to the levels of social capital available to their family, neighbourhood or community. The way in which it might be possible to quantify levels of social capital, for use as a single variable in future research into health and health-related behaviour, needs to be investigated further.

Many researchers are of the opinion that there needs to be a change of emphasis in health promotion research, that is, a shift in focus from changing individual behaviour towards making changes in the neighbourhood, community or social system (Gabbay, 1998; Gillies, 1997; Kawachi and Kennedy, 1997). Chapter 3 focused on social capital as a conceptual and analytical tool for investigating the wider determinants of health, that is, those factors over which the individual has limited control, such as poverty, income inequality and environmental problems. Smaller-scale studies have generally used a number of indicators to estimate the level of social capital available within a family or community, whereas epidemiological and larger-scale studies have made use of only one or two measures of social capital, notably 'trust' and 'group affiliation' (or 'civic engagement'). Levels of social trust are not, as yet, measured in any of the UK national social surveys, although use can be made of alternative indicators of social capital such as degree of satisfaction with the local social environment (see analyses in Part II). Furthermore, a number of researchers point out that, in US studies, 'group affiliation' is generally measured in terms of the types of organisations to which an individual belongs. Asking respondents to name specific organisations or activities, and to estimate how many hours they devote to them each week, would give a far more accurate indication of group affiliation.

In addition to a lack of research using UK data, other issues raised by this literature review include the need for more research into Putnam's argument that social capital – measured in terms of social trust and group affiliation – has declined since the end of World War II as a result of increased television viewing. Putnam's hypotheses have serious implications for health and health-related behaviour. The WHO's Jakarta Declaration (1997) makes it clear that sedentary lifestyles are a major health risk in many parts of the world, and claims that one of the ways in which good health might be promoted is through the generation of social capital, notably through community participation. However, not only does Putnam (1996) suggest that millions of people are becoming increasingly sedentary 'couch potatoes' as a result of excessive television viewing, but he also argues that television is encouraging people in the USA and elsewhere to play a less active role in community life. A number of researchers have questioned Putnam's arguments; for example, it has been suggested that certain types of community participation, such as taking part in single-issue campaigns, are increasing rather than decreasing (Schudson, 1996), and that new technologies will lead to increased rather than decreased social interaction – albeit at a distance. Furthermore it may well be that the rise in government-promoted individualistic ideology in both the UK and USA is more to blame for any recent decline in social trust and civic engagement than watching too much television. Nevertheless, there needs to be more research in order to determine whether social capital is in decline in the UK, and, if it is, what the reasons for this might be. Although a great deal of optimism has been generated by models of best practice, gaining an understanding of any potential barriers to building social capital is of paramount importance for those involved in health promotion.

Appendix: Methodology

This review of the literature relating to social support, social capital, health and health behaviour involved an extensive and systematic search of library catalogues, and of journals published during the past 20 years in the fields of medicine, nutrition, nursing, dentistry and the social and behavioural sciences. A number of text, CD-Rom and online databases were examined, including Sociofile, PsycLIT, and several Medline facilities. The website of the British Medical Association provided a link to a reliable, free-of-charge Medline, which gives unregistered users access to some full-text articles. In addition, certain full-text articles were obtained via the websites of the *British Medical Journal*, the *Journal of the American Medical Association* and *The Lancet*. The search-engines which consistently provided the most comprehensive results about research into social support and social capital were 'Excite' and 'Alta Vista'. The Social Sciences Information Gateway (SOSIG) also provided links to useful social science websites world-wide.

There is as yet no firm agreement among researchers as to the exact components of social capital. The debate is continuing, much of it conducted using the Internet as a forum, which itself is a manifestation of the type of social capital which has the potential to bridge a number of social chasms, including class, locality and ethnicity (Mitchell, 1996, cited in Gillies, 1997). Although the recent review of health promotion initiatives by Gillies (1997) demonstrates that the concept of social capital has world-wide applications, the majority of articles about social capital have appeared in American publications – most notably the online journal *The American Prospect* – and therefore tend to refer to organisations and activities which are specific to the USA. The collection of social capital literature is small in comparison with the volume of studies of social support or stress, and includes what Putnam has called 'the seemingly unrelated body of research on the sociology of economic development' (1995, p. 66). The British Library for Development Studies at the Institute of Development Studies (University of Sussex) has a collection of articles in this field. The Library Catalogue website address is: http://www.ids.ac.uk/bids/bids.htm

A particularly useful feature of the US online literature is that many full-text articles can be downloaded or printed directly from the screen. Links to other sites of interest are occasionally provided within the text, although some articles do not provide details of other authors' work which is cited in the text. Website addresses for publications which can be accessed in this way are given in the references to Part I, although it should be noted that these may be subject to change.

References

Please note that page numbers for articles which can be accessed via the Internet are 'as printed', and may vary if they are downloaded and printed later.

Abella, R and Heslin, R (1984). Health, locus of control, values and the behaviour of family and friends: an integrated approach to understanding health behaviour. *Basic and Applied Social Psychology* **5**: 283–93.

Aneshensel, C S, Pearlin, L I and Roberleigh, H S (1993). Stress, role captivity, and the cessation of caregiving. *Journal of Health and Social Behavior* **34**: 54–70.

Arber, S and Ginn, J (1990). The meaning of informal care: gender and the contribution of older people. *Ageing and Society* **12**(4): 429–54.

Arber, S and Ginn, J (1991). *Gender and Later Life: A Sociological Analysis of Resources and Constraints*. London: Sage.

Avison, W R and Turner, R J (1988). Stressful life events and depressive symptoms: disaggregating the effects of acute stressors and chronic strains. *Journal of Health and Social Behaviour* **29**: 253–64.

Barrera, M, Jr (1986). Distinctions between social support concepts, measures and models. *American Journal of Community Psychology* **14**(4): 413–45.

Belle, D (1987). 'Gender differences in the social moderators of stress', in: Barnett, R C, Biener, L and Baruch, G K (eds). *Gender and Stress*. New York: Free Press, pp. 257–77.

Berkman, L F (1984). Assessing the physical health effects of social networks and social supports. *Annual Review of Public Health* **5**: 413–32.

Berkman, L F (1985). 'The relationship of social networks and social support to morbidity and mortality', in: Cohen, S and Syme, L (eds). *Social Support and Health*. New York: Academic Press, pp. 241–62.

Berkman, L F and Breslow, L (1983). *Health and Ways of Living: The Alameda County Study*. New York and Oxford: Oxford University Press.

Berkman, L F and Syme, S L (1979). Social networks, host resistance and mortality: a nine-year follow-up study of Alameda County residents. *American Journal of Epidemiology* **109**: 186–204.

Billings, A G and Moos, R H (1984). The role of coping responses and social resources in attenuating the stress of life events. *Journal of Behavioural Medicine* **4**: 139–57.

Bourdieu, P (1986). *Forms of Capital*. New York: Free Press.

Brown, G W and Harris, T O (1978). *Social Origins of Depression: A Study of Psychiatric Disorder in Women*. London: Tavistock.

Campbell, D (1995). Social capital and sustainability: agriculture and communities in the Great Plains and Corn Belt (review article). *Sustainable Agriculture* **7**(4). Downloaded pages: 1–5.
http://www.sarep.ucdavis.edu/sarep/newsltr/v7n4/sa–7.htm

Cassell, J (1976). The contribution of the social environment to host resistance. *American Journal of Epidemiology* **104**: 107–23.

Cobb, S (1976). Social support as a moderator of life stress. *Psychosomatic Medicine* **38**(5): 300–14.

Cohen, S (1988). Psychosocial models of the role of social support in the etiology of physical disease. *Health Psychology* **7**: 269–97.

Cohen, S (1989). 'Social support and physical health: symptoms, health behaviors and infectious disease', in: Cummings, M, Greene, A L and Karraker, K H (eds). *Lifespan Developmental Psychology: Perspective on Stress and Coping*. Hillside, NJ: Lawrence Erlbaum.

Cohen, S and McKay, G (1984). 'Social support, stress and the buffering hypothesis: a theoretical analysis', in: Baum, A, Singer, J E and Taylor, S E (eds) (1984). *Handbook of Psychology and Health*. Hillside, NJ: Lawrence Erlbaum, pp. 253–67.

Cohen, S and Syme, L (eds) (1985). *Social Support and Health*. New York: Academic Press.

Cohen, S and Williamson, G M (1991). Stress and infectious disease in humans. *Psychological Bulletin* **109**(1): 5–24.

Cohen, S and Wills, T A (1985). Stress, social support and the buffering hypothesis. *Psychological Bulletin* **98**: 310–57.

Cohen, S, Doyle, W J, Skone, D P, Rabin, B S and Gwaltney, J M Jr (1997). Social ties and susceptibility to the common cold. *Journal of the American Medical Association* **277**: 1940–44.

Coleman, J S (1988). Social capital in the creation of human capital. *American Journal of Sociology* **94**: supplement S95–S120.

Coronary Prevention Group (1997). *UK Charter for Health Promotion*: National Consultation Draft, pp. 1–4.
http://www.healthnet.org.uk/media/press/charterlocal.htm

Colhoun, H and Prescott-Clarke, P (eds) (1996). *Health Survey for England 1994*. London: HMSO.

Cox, E (1997). Building social capital. *Health Promotion Matters*. No. 4, September 1997. Downloaded pages: 1–5.
http://www.vichealth.vic.gov.au/HPM/issue4/article1.html

Coyne, J C and Downey, G (1991). Social factors and psychopathology: stress, social support and coping processes. *Annual Review of Psychology* **42**: 401–25.

Creed, F (1985). Life events and physical illness. *Journal of Psychosomatic Research* **29**(2): 113–23.

Crohan, S and Antonucci, T (1989). 'Friends as a source of support in old age', in: Adams, R and Blieszner, R (eds) (1989). *Older Adult Friendship*. London: Sage, pp. 129–46.

Daly, J (1997). Social factors in evaluating health promotion. *Health Promotion Matters*. No. 2, July 1997. Downloaded pages: 1–5.
http://www.vichealth.vic.gov.au/HPM/issue2/article1.html

Diehr, P, Koepsell, T, Cheadle, A, Patsy, B M, Wagner, E and Curry, S (1993). Do communities differ in health behaviors? *Journal of Clinical Epidemiology* **46**(10): 1141–9.

Drever, F and Whitehead, M (eds) (1997). *Health Inequalities: Decennial Supplement*. London: Stationery Office.

Dunkel-Schetter, C and Bennett, T L (1990). 'Differentiating the cognitive and behavioral aspects of social support', in: Sarason, B R, Sarason, I G and Pierce, G R (eds) (1990). *Social Support: An Interactional View*. New York: Wiley, pp. 267–96.

Ellaway, A and McIntyre, S (1996). Does where you live predict health related behaviours?: a case study in Glasgow. *Health Bulletin (Edinburgh)* **54**(6): 443–6.

Evans, G W, Palsane, M N, Lepore, S J and Martin, J (1989). Residential density and psychological health: the mediating effects of social support. *Journal of Personality and Social Psychology* **57**(6): 994–9.

Flaherty, J and Richman, J (1989). Gender differences in the perception and utilization of social support: theoretical perspectives and an empirical test. *Social Science and Medicine* **28**(12): 1221–8.

Flora, C B (1995). *Social Capital and Sustainability: Agriculture and Communities in the Great Plains and Corn Belt.* Journal Paper No. J16309. Iowa Agriculture and Home Economics Experiment Station, Ames, Iowa (Project No. 3281). Downloaded pages: 1–5.
Access via Campbell D (1995): http://www.sarep.ucdavis.edu/sarep/newsltr/v7n4/sa–7.htm

Gabbay, J (1998). Our healthier nation can be achieved if the demands allow it. *British Medical Journal* **316** (7130). Downloaded pages: 1–3.
http://www.bmj.com/bmj/archive/7130/7130el.htm

Ganster, D C and Victor, B (1988). The impact of social support on mental and physical health. *British Journal of Medical Psychology* **61**: 17–36.

Gillies, P A (1996). 'The contribution of social and behavioural science to the prevention of HIV', in: Mann, J and Tarantola, D J M (eds) (1996). *AIDS in the World,* vol. 2. New York: Oxford University Press.

Gillies, P A (1997). *The Effectiveness of Alliances and Partnerships for Health Promotion.* Conference Working Paper. London: World Health Organization and Health Education Authority.

Ginn, J, Arber, S and Cooper, H (1997). *Researching Older People's Health Needs and Health Promotion Issues.* London: Health Education Authority.

Gottlieb, B H (ed.) (1983). *Social Support Strategies.* Beverly Hills, Calif.: Sage.

Gottlieb, B H (1988). *Marshalling Social Support: Formats, Processes and Effects.* Newbury Park, Calif.: Sage.

Gottlieb, N H and Baker, J A (1986). The relative influence of health beliefs, parental and peer behaviors and exercise participation on smoking, alcohol use and physical activity. *Social Science and Medicine.* **22**(9): 915–27.

Health Education Authority (1995). *Health and Lifestyles: A Survey of the UK Population,* Part 1. London: HEA.

Helsing, K and Szklo, M (1981). Mortality after bereavement. *American Journal of Epidemiology.* **114**: 41–52.

Hibbard, J H (1985). Social ties and health status: an examination of moderating factors. *Health Education Quarterly* **12**(1): 23–34.

Hogan, J M (1998). Untitled abstract. *Social Capital – Bridging Disciplines, Policies and Communities.* International Conference, Michigan State University, 20–22 April 1998: abstracts, pp. 23–6.
http://www.jsri.msu.edu/soccap/Abstracts.htm

Holmes, T H and Rahe, R H (1967). The social readjustment rating scale. *Journal of Psychosomatic Research* **11**: 213–18.

House, J S (1981). *Work, Stress and Social Support.* Reading, Mass.: Addison-Wesley.

House, J S and Kahn, R (1985). 'Measures and concepts of social support', in: Cohen, S and Syme, L (eds) (1985). *Social Support and Health.* New York: Academic Press, pp. 83–108.

House, J S, Robbins, C and Metzner, H L (1982). The association of social relationships and activities with mortality: prospective evidence from the Tecumseh community health study. *American Journal of Epidemiology* **116**: 123–40.

House, J S, Landis, K R and Umberson, D (1988). Social relationships and health. *Science* **214**: 540–5.

Hyden, G (1998): The social capital crash in the periphery: an analysis of the current predicament in sub-Saharan Africa. *Social Capital – Bridging Disciplines, Policies and Communities.* International Conference, Michigan State University, 20–22 April 1998: abstracts, pp. 28–30.
http://www.jsri.msu.edu/soccap/Abstracts.htm

Jerrome, D (1990). The significance of friendship for women in later life. *Ageing and Society* **5**(1): 51–64.

Kari, N, Boyte, H C, Jennings, B with Colbert, T, Garland, M, Hassin, H, Mitchell, M, O'Neil, E, Severoni, E and Sirianni, C (1994). Health as a civic question. *American Civic Forum.* 28 November. Downloaded pages: 1–18.
http://fount.journalism.wisc.edu/cpn/sections/topics/health/civic_perspectives/health_as_quest.html

Kawachi, I and Kennedy, B P (1997). Health and social cohesion: Why care about income inequality? *British Medical Journal* **314**: 1037–40.

Kawachi, I, Kennedy, B P and Lochner, K (1997). Long Live Community: social capital as public health. *The American Prospect.* No. 35 (November–December): 55–9. Downloaded pages: 1–6.
http://epn.org/prospect/35/35kawanf.html

Kennedy, B P, Kawachi I and Prothrow-Stith, D (1996). Income distribution and mortality: cross-sectional ecological study of the Robin Hood Index in the United States. *British Medical Journal* **312**: 1013–14.

Kessler, R C and McLeod, J (1984). 'The costs of caring: a perspective on the relationship between sex and psychological distress', in: Sarason, I G and Sarason, B R (eds) (1984). *Social Support: Theory, Research and Applications.* The Hague: Martinus Nijhof.

Kessler, R C, Price, R H and Wortman, C B (1985). Social factors in psychopathology: stress, social support, and coping processes. *Annual Review of Psychology* **36**: 531–72.

Kreuter, M with Lezin, N and Baker, B (1998). Is social capital a mediating structure for effective community-based health promotion? *Atlanta 2000/Harris Training and Consulting Services (HTCS).* Downloaded pages: 1–4.
http://www.htcs.com/soccap.htm

Kulik, J A and Mahler, H I M (1989). Social support and recovery from surgery. *Health Psychology* **8**: 221–38.

Lin, N and Ensel, W M (1989). Life stress and health: stress and resources. *American Sociological Review* **54**: 382–99.

Lin, N, Dean, A and Ensel, W M (1986). *Social Support, Life Events and Depression.* New York/London: Academic Press.

McBride, C M, Curry, S J, Grothaus, L C, Nelson, J C, Lando, H and Pirie, P L (1998). Partner smoking status and pregnant smokers' perceptions of support for and likelihood of smoking cessation. *Health Psychology* **17**(1): 63–9.

McGloshen, T H and O'Bryant, S I (1988). The psychological well-being of older, recent widows. P*sychology of Women Quarterly* **12**(1): 99–116.

McLeod, J D and Kessler, R C (1990). Socioeconomic status differences in vulnerability to undesirable life events. *Journal of Health and Social Behaviour* **23**: 220–34.

Madge, N and Marmot, M (1987). Psychosocial factors and health. *Journal of Social Affairs* **5**: 81–134.

Marmot, M G and Morris, J N (1985). 'The social environment', in: Holland, W W, Detels, R and Knox, G (eds) (1985). *Oxford Textbook of Public Health*, vol. 1. Oxford: Oxford University Press.

Merry, S E (1984). 'Rethinking gossip and scandal', in: Black, D (ed.) (1984). *Toward a General Theory of Social Control*, vol. 1: *Fundamentals.* New York: Academic Press, pp. 271–302.

Mirowsky, J and Ross, C E (1989). *Social Causes of Psychological Distress.* New York: Aldine de Gruyter.

Mitchell, W J (1996). *City of Bits, Space, Place and the Infobahn*. Cambridge, Mass.: MIT Press.

Morgan, S L (1998). Untitled abstract. *Social Capital – Bridging Disciplines, Policies and Communities*. International Conference, Michigan State University, 20–22 April 1998: abstracts, pp. 39–41. http://www.jsri.msu.edu/soccap/Abstracts.htm

OPCS (1996). *Living in Britain: Results from the 1994 General Household Survey*. London: HMSO.

Orth-Gomer, K, Perski, A and Theorell, T (1983). Psychosocial factors and cardiovascular disease – a review of the current state of our knowledge. *Stress Research Reports No. 165*. Stockholm: Laboratory for Clinical Stress Research.

Parsons, T (1975). The sick role and the role of the physician reconsidered. *Milbank Memorial Fund Quarterly* **53**: 257–78.

Pearlin, L I (1989). The sociological study of stress. *Journal of Health and Social Behaviour* **30**: 241–56.

Pearlin, L I and Johnson, J S (1977). Marital status, life strains and depression. *American Sociological Review* **42**: 704–15.

Portes, A and Landolt, P (1996). The downside of social capital. *The American Prospect,* No. 26 (May–June 1996). Downloaded pages: 1–5.
http://epn.org/prospect/26/26–cnt2.html

Putnam, R D (1993). The prosperous community: social capital and public life. *The American Prospect*, No. 13 (Spring 1993). Downloaded pages: 1–8.
http://epn.org/prospect/13/13putn.html

Putnam, R D (1995). Bowling alone: America's declining social capital. *Journal of Democracy* **6**: 65–78.
http://muse.jhu.edu/demo/journal_of_democracy/v006/putnam.html

Putnam, R D (1996). The strange disappearance of civic America. *The American Prospect*, No. 24 (Winter 1996). Downloaded pages: 1–17.
http://epn.org/prospect/24/24putn.html

Putnam, R D with Leonardi, R and Nanetti, R Y (1993). *Making Democracy Work: Civic Traditions in Modern Italy.* Princeton, NJ: Princeton University Press.

Reissman, C K (1990). *Divorce Talk: Women and Men Make Sense of Personal Relationships.* New Brunswick, NJ: Rutgers University Press.

Rook, K (1992). 'Detrimental aspects of social relationships: taking stock of an emerging literature', in: Veiel, H O F and Baumann, U (eds) (1992). *The Meaning and Measurement of Social Support*. New York: Hemisphere, pp. 157–70.

Ross, C E and Mirowsky, J (1989). Explaining the social patterns of depression: control and problem solving – or support and talking? *Journal of Health and Social Behavior* **30**: 206–19.

Runyan, D K, Hunter, W M, Socolar, R S, Amaya-Jackson, I, English, D, Lansverk, J, Dubowitz, H, Browne, D H, Bangdiwala, S I and Mathew, R M (1998). Children who prosper in unfavorable environments: the relationship to social capital. *Pediatrics* **101**: 12–18

Sampson, R J, Raudenbush, S W and Earls, F (1997). Neighborhoods and violent crime: a multilevel study of collective efficacy. *Science* **277**: 918–24.

Sarason, B R, Pierce, G R and Sarason, I G (1990). 'Social support: the sense of acceptance and the role of relationships', in: Sarason, B R, Sarason, I G and Pierce, G R (eds) (1990). *Social Support: An Interactional View.* New York: Wiley, pp. 97–128.

Schudson, M (1996). What if civic life didn't die? *The American Prospect*, No. 25 (March–April 1996): 17–20. Downloaded pages: 1–5.
http://epn.org/prospect/25/25-cnt1.html

Schwarzer, R and Leppin, A (1992). 'Possible impact of social ties and support on morbidity and mortality', in: Vieil, H O F and Baumann, U (eds) (1992). *The Meaning and Measurement of Social Support*. New York: Hemisphere, pp. 65–83.

Silver, R L, Boon, C and Stones, M H (1983). Searching for meaning in misfortune: making sense of incest. *Journal of Social Issues* **39**(2): 81–102.

Skocpol, T (1996). Unravelling from above. *The American Prospect*, No. 25 (March–April 1996): 20–5. Downloaded pages: 1–7.
http://epn.org/prospect/25/25-cnt2.html

Stanton, W R and McGee, R (1996). Adolescents' promotion of nonsmoking and smoking. *Addiction and Behaviour* **21**(1): 47–56.

Tausig, M (1983). 'Measuring life events', in: Lin, N, Dean, A and Ensel, W M (eds) (1983). *Social Support, Life Events and Depression*. New York/London: Academic Press, pp. 71–93.

Thoits, P A (1982). Conceptual, methodological and theoretical problems in studying social support as a buffer against life stress. *Journal of Health and Social Behavior* **23**: 145–59.

Thoits, P A (1983). 'Dimensions of life events that influence psychological distress: an evaluation and synthesis of the literature', in: Kaplan, H B (ed.) (1983). *Psychosocial Stress: Trends in Theory and Research*. New York: Academic Press, pp. 33–103.

Thoits, P A (1984). Explaining distribution of psychological vulnerability: lack of social support in the face of life stress. *Social Forces* **63**: 453–81.

Thoits, P A (1985). 'Social support processes and psychological wellbeing: theoretical possibilities', in: Sarason, I G and Sarason, B R (eds) (1985). *Social Support: Theory, Research and Applications*. The Hague: Martinus Nijhof, pp. 51–72.

Thoits, P A (1987). Gender and marital status differences in control and distress: common stress versus unique stress explanations. *Journal of Health and Social Behavior* **28**: 7–22.

Thoits, P A (1992). Identity structures and psychological wellbeing: gender and marital status comparisons. *Social Psychology Quarterly* **55**(3): 236–56.

Thoits, P A (1994). Stressors and problem-solving: the individual as psychological activist. *Journal of Health and Social Behavior* **35**: 143–59.

Thoits, P A (1995). Stress, coping, and social support processes: Where are we? What next? *Journal of Health and Social Behavior*: Extra issue: 53–79.

Tocqueville, A de (1966). *Democracy in America*. New York: Harper.

Townsend, P, Davidson, N and Whitehead, M (eds) (1988). *Inequalities in Health: 'The Black Report' and The Health Divide*. Harmondsworth: Penguin Books.

Turner, R J and Avison, W R (1989). Gender and depression: assessing exposure and vulnerability to life events in a chronically strained population. *Journal of Nervous and Mental Disease* **177**(8): 443–55.

Turner, R J and Avison, W R (1992). Innovations in the measurement of life stress: Crisis Theory and the significance of event resolution. *Journal of Health and Social Behavior* **33**: 36–50.

Turner, R J and Marino, F (1994). Social support and social structure: a descriptive epidemiology. *Journal of Health and Social Behavior* **35**: 193–212.

Turner, R J, Wheaton, B and Lloyd, D A (1995). The epidemiology of social stress. *American Sociological Review* **60**: 104–24.

Uchino, B N, Cacioppo, J T and Kiecolt-Glaser, J K (1996). The relationship between social support and physiological processes: a review with emphasis on underlying mechanisms and implications for health. *Psychological Bulletin* **119**(3): 488–531.

Umberson, D (1992). Gender, marital status and the social control of health behavior. *Social Science and Medicine* **34**(8): 907–17.

Vaux, A (1988). *Social Support: Theory, Research and Intervention*. New York: Praeger.

Ward, A W M (1976). Mortality of bereavement. *British Medical Journal* **1**: 700–2.

Waring, E M (1985). Editorial. *Psychological Medicine* **15**: 9–14.

Wethington, E and Kessler, R C (1986). Perceived support, received support and adjustment to stressful life events. *Journal of Health and Social Behavior* **27**: 78–89.

Wilkinson, R G (1992). Income distribution and life expectancy. *British Medical Journal* **304**: 165–8.

Wilkinson, R G (1996). *Unhealthy Societies: The Afflictions of Inequality*. London: Routledge.

Wills, T A (1985). 'Supportive functions of interpersonal relations', in: Cohen, S and Syme, L (eds) (1985). *Social Support and Health*. New York: Academic Press, pp. 61–82.

Wills, T A and Vaughan, R (1989). Social support and substance use in early adolescence. *Journal of Behavioral Medicine* **12**(4): 321–39.

Wise, G (1986). Overcoming loneliness. *Nursing Times* **82**(22): 37–42.

World Health Organization (1997). The Jakarta Declaration on Leading Health Promotion into the 21st Century. Fourth International Conference on Health Promotion, 21–25 July 1997.
http://rubble.ultralab.anglia.ac.uk/declare.htm

PART II

Secondary analysis of British data

Helen Cooper, Sara Arber and Jay Ginn

Summary of Part II

Part I provided a literature review of research on the links between social support and social capital in relation to health and health-related behaviour. Part II examines social support and social capital in relation to health and health-related behaviour using three British national datasets: the HEA Health and Lifestyles Survey (HALS) for 1992, the Health Survey of England (HSE) for 1993–4, and the General Household Survey (GHS) for 1994.

Material living conditions and socioeconomic position were found to be much stronger predictors of adverse health than measures of social capital and social support in these surveys.

Out of four measures of social capital derived from the HEA HALS, the strongest associations with health were found using an index of the individual's perception of their 'neighbourhood social capital'. Social capital influences the health and reported stress of women to a greater extent than for men. This suggests that women's health is more affected by the quality of their neighbourhood than is the case for men, and that low social capital contributes to feelings of stress among women. Women living in neighbourhoods which they perceive to be high in social capital were less likely to smoke, after controlling for material deprivation and socioeconomic factors. Community participation was strongly associated with lower smoking among men and women.

Social support based on contact with friends was more important than contact with relatives for influencing health, but a more subjective indicator of social support based on personal feelings about friends and relatives was a more important factor in influencing health than the amount of contact. There was no evidence that social support reduced levels of stress after controlling for poor material living conditions and socioeconomic position. Perceived social support from friends and relatives was associated with lower levels of smoking and a better diet, after adjusting for socioeconomic variables which are strongly linked to these two health behaviours.

Recommendations

1. Future health surveys should include measures of social capital, for example, the measure of neighbourhood social capital derived from the HEA Health and Lifestyles Survey. More information about the extent of community participation in a wider range of activities and over a longer time period than two weeks would also be valuable. In addition, indicators of social capital which relate to perceptions of trust and security should be added to future surveys.

2. Surveys should clearly distinguish between the collection of different types of social support measures. The more important measures relate to *perceived* closeness of relationships with friends and relatives, and the frequency of contact with *friends* asked separately from frequency of contact with relatives.

3. Measures of social capital and social support are related to an individual's age, gender, socioeconomic circumstances and material living conditions. It is therefore essential that surveys collect information about all these variables, and examine the contribution of social capital and social support to health and health-related behaviour after adjusting for these structural factors.

4. It is important to measure social capital at both the individual level, using surveys (as in Chapters 5–8), and at the aggregate area or community level. Surveys should include area level information based, for example, on ACORN classifications or derived from ward or enumeration district data from the population census. In this way, it will be possible to undertake multi-level analysis, in order to identify the effects on health of the quality of the area of residence separately from the effects of the individual's perception of their neighbourhood.

5. The present report has not considered black and minority ethnic groups. There is an urgent need to examine the links between social support and social capital in relation to the health and health-related behaviour of members of black and minority ethnic groups.

5. Conceptualising social capital and social support using British survey data

The relative influence of structural factors on health and lifestyle has been the subject of extensive debate in Britain (Townsend, Phillimore and Beattie, 1988; Wilkinson, 1996). There is substantial evidence that low social class and poor material living conditions adversely influence health and health behaviour, but much less is known about the contribution of social capital and social support (see Part I).

Based on data from three large-scale British surveys, Part II examines the independent effects of measures of social support and of social capital on health and health behaviour, after taking into account the social and economic characteristics of the individual and their household. A particular focus is placed on how gender differentiates the pattern of these relationships and whether social capital and social support vary according to age and structural characteristics. The analysis identifies those with particularly poor social support and low levels of social capital, as well as those most likely to be in poor health and engaging in health-damaging behaviour.

One limitation to research in this area has been confusion and considerable diversity in the definition and measurement of both social support and social capital (see Part I). In this chapter, we firstly discuss the datasets used in our analysis: the HEA Health and Lifestyles Survey, the Health Survey for England and the General Household Survey. Secondly, we consider how the concepts of social support and social capital can be measured using data from the HEA Health and Lifestyles Survey, highlighting the analytic limitations of these measures. It is unlikely that each individual will have equal access to social support and social capital; therefore we analyse how these vary for men and women according to their age and key socio-demographic and socioeconomic characteristics.

Datasets and analysis

The research involves the analysis of three complementary national datasets. The age distribution of men and women in each dataset is shown in Table 5.1.

Table 5.1. Percentage of men and women in each dataset by age group

	HALS, 1992		HSE, 1993–1994		GHS, 1994	
Age	Men	Women	Men	Women	Men	Women
16–24	19.1	17.9	13.5	12.6	–	–
25–34	21.7	21.0	19.8	19.8	–	–
35–44	18.4	18.1	18.1	17.6	–	–
45–54	16.3	16.1	16.4	15.4	–	–
55–64	13.7	13.8	14.0	12.5	–	–
65–74	10.8	13	11.9	12.6	65.4	56.3
75–84	–	–	5.2	7.4	28.4	32.3
85+	–	–	0.9	2.0	6.1	11.4
%	100.0	100.0	100.0	100.0	100.0	100.0
N =	2487	2520	14 867	17 507	1505	2125

Investigating social capital and social support based on a secondary analysis of these national datasets means that we are limited to the original questions included in the surveys, which were not directly designed to address the issues being examined in this research. There are also differences between the surveys in how some concepts are measured. For example, social class in the HEA Health and Lifestyles Survey is based on the Registrar General's classification and most non-employed individuals are excluded from this measure (see Appendix A), whereas the General Household Survey and the Health Survey for England collect social class information based on current or last main job using a measure of socioeconomic group (SEG) (see Appendices B and C).

Our analysis uses cross-tabulation to provide an understanding of the pattern of relationships, and these results are presented as figures and tables in each chapter. Actual percentage values have been included on the figures (rounded to the nearest whole number), and, where this was not appropriate, the percentages are given in tables in Appendix E. In addition, multivariate logistic regression analysis is used to examine the relative influence of social capital and social support on health and health behaviour by statistically controlling for other relevant factors, such as age and socioeconomic position. Further information about this procedure and how to interpret the results of logistic regression analysis is given in Appendix D.

1. The HEA Health and Lifestyles Survey, 1992

The HEA Health and Lifestyle Survey (HALS) was conducted by MORI in 1992 with a response rate of 75% (HEA, 1995). Interview data were obtained from 5004 men and women aged 16–74 years and the data were weighted proportional to the household size of each respondent. This survey asks respondents about the type and quality of social contact with friends and relatives. It also contains information on community activity, length of residence and the individuals' perception of the quality of their neighbourhood, which form the basis of our social capital measures. The HALS data include measures of reported stress, health status and smoking as well as socioeconomic measures, such as social class, material deprivation and employment status.

2. The Health Survey for England, 1993 and 1994

The Health Survey for England (HSE) is an annual interview survey of adults living in about 10 000 private households in England (Colhoun and Prescott-Clarke, 1996). Combining two years of HSE data (1993 and 1994) gives a large sample of over 30 000 individuals aged 16 and above. The survey contains detailed questions on diet and smoking, as well as a series of questions about perceived social support from friends and relatives. This information can be related to an individual's socioeconomic position, level of reported stress and health status.

3. The General Household Survey, 1994

The 1994 General Household Survey (GHS) contains a special section for people aged over 65 which includes questions about their ability to perform tasks of daily living and frequency of contact with neighbours, friends and relatives (Bennett *et al.,* 1996). The GHS does not ask these questions related to social support of respondents below 65. Our analysis is therefore restricted to the over 3000 older people living in private households in Britain. The survey also includes information about their current smoking behaviour which can be related to a range of socioeconomic measures including income, housing tenure, occupational class and living arrangements.

Measuring social capital

Social capital is conceptualised as a 'community resource' which is created from everyday social interactions and social networks and is founded upon the principles of trust, reciprocity and community participation for mutual benefit (Putnam, 1993; Bullen and Onyx, 1998). Social capital is a multi-dimensional concept and may include the collective economic and cultural resources available to a community as well as the level of social trust and social support networks (Putnam, 1993). A detailed review of research literature on social capital is provided in Part I.

Based on large-scale surveys in the US, many researchers have measured social capital according to reported levels of social trust and group affiliation (Putnam, 1996; Kennedy, Kawachi and Prothrow-Stith, 1996; Coleman, 1988). Others have used church membership and neighbourhood support to measure community involvement and social interaction (Runyan, 1998).

Bullen and Onyx (1998) conducted an exploratory survey to identify the underlying elements of social capital. Based on adults aged 18–65 living in one of five communities in New South Wales, Australia, a total of eight factors were found to capture 'social capital'. These were: participation in the local community, proactivity in a social context, feelings of trust and safety, neighbourhood connections, connections with family and friends, tolerance of diversity and value of life and work connections.

The Health and Lifestyles Survey (HALS) does not contain any questions on social trust, tolerance or perceived value of life or work which could be used to indicate social capital. However, respondents are asked six questions about the area in which they live: whether they enjoy living in their neighbourhood, if neighbours look after one another, whether they perceive the area to be safe and to have good facilities for young children, leisure and transport. Responses to these six questions were combined (see Appendix A) and used to provide an index of social capital in the individual's neighbourhood. It is important to note that this is a measure of the *individual's perception* of the level of social capital in their neighbourhood, rather than an area-level characteristic of the surrounding environment. In addition, the components of our neighbourhood social capital scale may be culturally specific and may not be gender neutral; for example, women may be more aware of issues relating to personal safety than men.

Respondents who perceive their environment as being safe to live in, with good facilities and strong neighbourhood ties benefit from living in an area with a high level of social capital, whereas those who report that they feel unsafe, lack community facilities and neighbourhood support do not. For our analysis we distinguish between four levels of perceived social capital based on their scored response: low (score –6 to 0), medium (score 1–2), high (score 3–4) and very high (score of 5–6) – see Appendix A. We refer to this measure as *neighbourhood social capital.*

Quantitative indicators of social capital, based on surveys of individuals, complement existing aggregate level analyses of social capital (see Part I) and allow the distribution of social capital to be analysed based on large and representative samples of the population. They also provide a valuable supplement to qualitative work based on small localised communities. However, any attempt to capture the complexity of a social environment within an empirically derived scale has limitations, and a neighbourhood social capital score cannot adequately reflect all the different dimensions of social experience within an individual's local community (Bullen and Onyx, 1998). To improve our measurement of social capital we supplemented the above index with other measures from HALS relating to community activity, social integration and experience of crime and/or attack.

Community activity was measured according to whether or not the respondent participated in a voluntary or community group, was involved in any religious activities or attended an adult education class in the last two weeks (see Appendix A). Putnam (1993) suggests that involvement in community activities or 'civic engagement' may develop new social networks and facilitate the development of social capital through shared norms, trust and reciprocity. This HALS measure is based only on reported community activity in the last two weeks; it provides no indicator of the time devoted to this activity or the individual's role within the community or voluntary group.

We distinguish 'social integration' from social support relating to contact with friends and relatives, which is discussed later. We assessed *social integration* indirectly according to the length of time an individual had been living in the area, which we assume is related to involvement in informal social networks. Putnam (1996) argues that residential mobility and difficulties in 'putting down roots' in a new community have an important bearing on social capital, as measured by levels of social trust and group affiliation. We distinguished between those who had been resident for one year or less compared with an intermediate period of residency (2–3 years and 4–9 years) and long-term residency of 10 years or more.

It has been argued that when social capital is high and members of a community have a common understanding and adherence to social norms, then the level of crime and violence is very low (Sampson, Raudenbush and Earls, 1997). Questions in HALS ask respondents whether or not they have experienced theft, mugging, break-in or another crime, or whether they have suffered racist abuse or physical attack in the last year. Positive responses to any of these questions are combined in our analysis and are taken to indicate low social capital, as shown by *experience of crime or attack.*

The social correlates of social capital

Previous research based on large-scale surveys has shown that social capital increases with advancing age (Putnam, 1996) and this is confirmed in the HALS data using our measure of neighbourhood social capital. Figure 5.1 shows that the percentage of men and women with high social capital varies significantly according to their age. Over half of older people aged 55–74 years report high social capital compared with 36% of women and only 27% of men aged 16–24 years. Older age groups may have more favourable perceptions of their living environment or be more likely to live in better-quality areas than younger people. Women aged between 16 and 34 years are more likely to have high social capital than men of the same age, but between the ages of 35 and 64 there is little gender difference, with men slightly more likely to have high social capital than women in the oldest age group.

Participation in community activities is also more likely with increasing age, especially for women. Figure 5.2 shows that older women are much more likely to participate in a community activity than their younger counterparts, with approximately one-third aged between 45 and 74 involved in voluntary, religious or community groups in the last two weeks, compared with 24% of women aged 35–44 and only 12% aged 16–24 years. Men aged 25 and above have a much lower level of community participation than women, and although community activity increases from 14% to 20% between the ages of 25–34 and 35–44 years, for men there is no further increase with advancing age.

The age-related increase in social capital and the greater community participation of older women supports results from US survey data showing greater levels of social trust and community participation among older adults. Putnam (1996) argues that these age differences represent a generational decline in social trust and social capital rather than differences due to stage in the life course, but it is impossible to assess these arguments in our study based on cross-sectional data.

The increased labour market participation of women has been highlighted by Putnam (1996) as one factor associated with the decline in social capital over time. He argues that women who traditionally were most actively involved in facilitating local community activity and social networks are now more likely to enter paid employment and centre their social activity and networking around the workplace (Putnam 1996; Skocpol, 1996). In spite of the increasing employment participation of British women, they are nevertheless much more likely to be involved in community activities than men (see Figure 5.2).

In Britain there is little variation in neighbourhood social capital according to employment status, apart from very low levels reported by the unemployed. Figure 5.3 shows about half of all men and women have a high social capital score, with the exception of the unemployed. For both sexes, being unemployed is associated with decreased social capital, with only 40% of women and 37% of men scoring 3 or more on our scale.

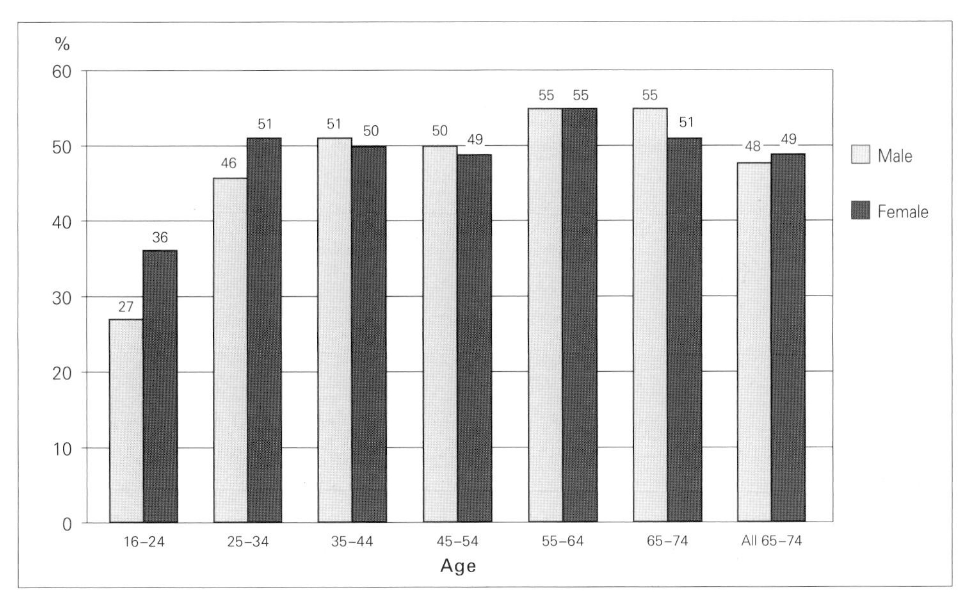

P < 0.001 for men and women

Source: HEA Health and Lifestyles Survey, 1992

***Fig. 5.1.* Percentage with high neighbourhood social capital (score 3+) by age and sex**

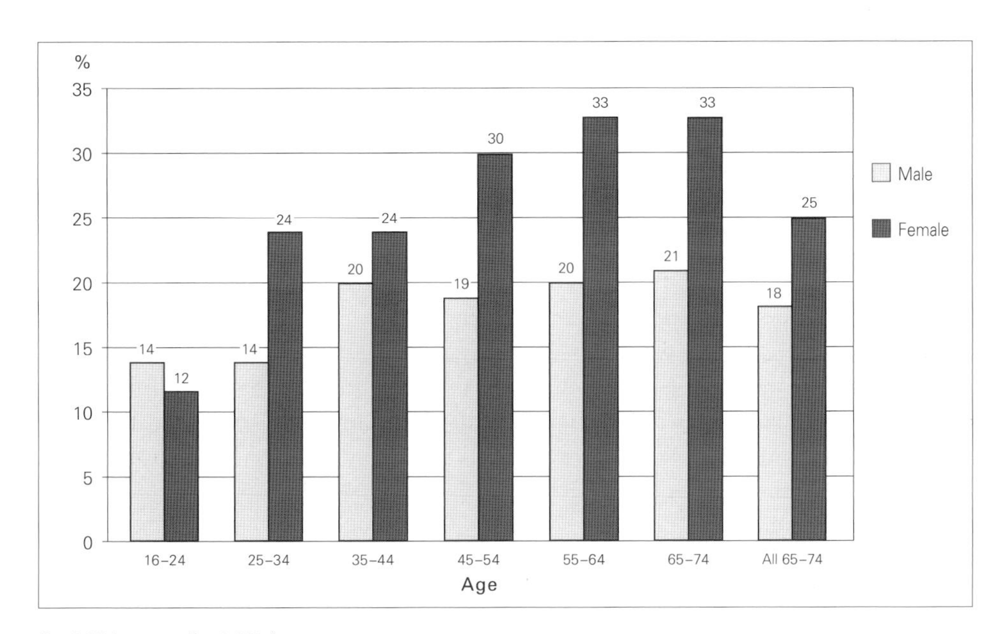

P < 0.05 for men; *P* < 0.001 for women

Source: HEA Health and Lifestyles Survey, 1992

***Fig. 5.2.* Percentage currently involved in community activity by age and sex**

Our results show that economic inactivity because of retirement, looking after the home or being in full-time education is not associated with lower neighbourhood social capital relative to those in paid employment. However, social capital is markedly reduced among unemployed men and women who are excluded from the paid labour force. Putnam's (1996) analysis of the American General Social Survey (GSS) did not distinguish between the unemployed and the economically inactive, but the former may have a more severe lack of financial resources and be more likely to live in a poorer quality neighbourhood.

Figure 5.4 clearly shows much lower community participation among the unemployed compared with the employed and the economically inactive. This is particularly marked for women, with community participation three times more likely among women who work full-time (21%) and nearly four times as great for women who are non-employed or employed part-time compared with the unemployed. Unlike Putnam (1996) our results do not suggest that paid employment erodes neighbourhood social capital and community participation, as part-time work is positively associated with both of these measures. However, those who are unable to find paid work are less actively involved in community activity and rate their living environment more negatively. To the extent that our measure of neighbourhood social capital provides an indicator of area-level characteristics, we would expect even lower social capital among the unemployed living in areas with high unemployment. For example, an individual without paid work will still benefit from living in a safe area, whilst an area with few community facilities is likely to be perceived less favourably by the employed and unemployed alike.

Measuring social support

The concept of social support has been measured in numerous ways by researchers, but a common approach is to distinguish between its 'structural' and 'functional' components. The former denotes the way in which social networks are organised and composed, the frequency of contact with friends and relatives and participation in social activity (House and Kahn, 1985; Barrera, 1986; House, Landis and Umberson, 1988). The functions of social support include the availability of network members for practical help, information and emotional support. A further distinction is often made between social support that is 'perceived' to exist by the individual and actual 'received' social support (see Part I).

The main limitation of using HALS data to measure social support is that the questions were originally designed as indicators of 'psychosocial health'. Respondents are asked whether they have any close friends and close relatives that they see or speak to on a regular basis (where 'regular' is defined by the respondent). Using this information we

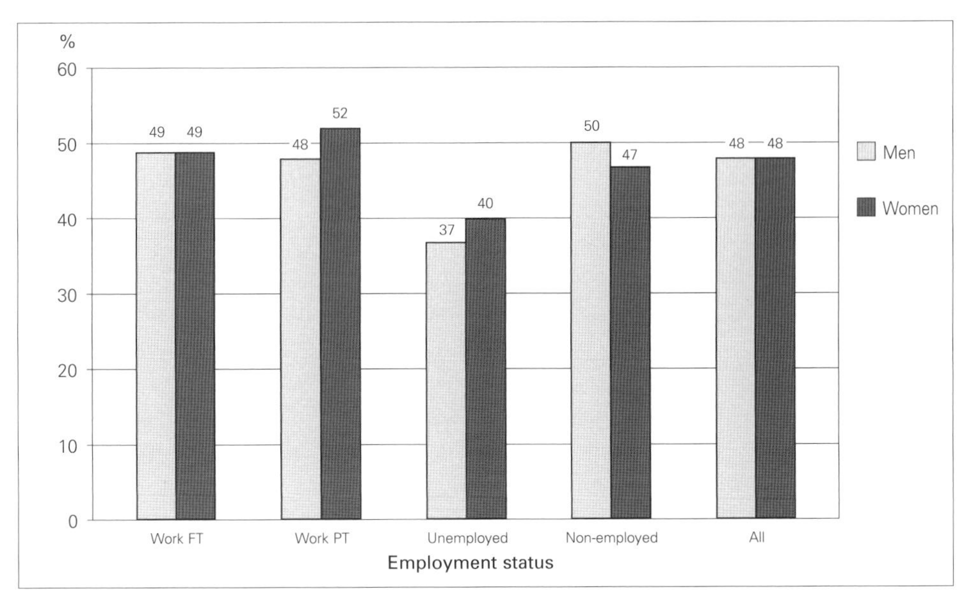

P < 0.001 for men and women
Source: HEA Health and Lifestyles Survey, 1992

***Fig. 5.3.* Percentage with high neighbourhood social capital (score 3+) by employment status: men and women aged 16–74 years**

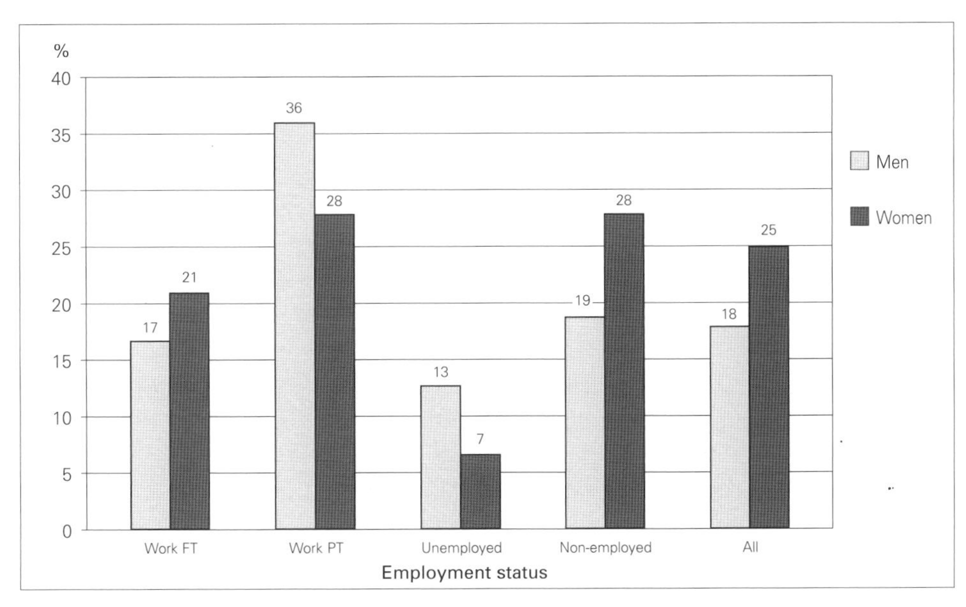

P < 0.001 for men and women
Source: HEA Health and Lifestyles Survey, 1992

Fig. 5.4. Percentage currently involved in community activity by employment status: men and women aged 16–74 years

distinguished between those who say they have close friends and relatives, those with close relatives only, close friends only, and those who are not in close contact with friends or relatives (see Appendix A). It could be argued that this measure of *perceived close contact* covers a structural aspect of social support, by indicating the relative importance of friends and relatives in their social network, as well as perceived social support.

However, O'Reilly (1988) argues that an individual's social network has multiple functions, of which social support is only one, and each of these should therefore be viewed as distinct concepts. The HALS data do not allow us to specify the different dimensions of social support that may be received from social network members, for example, whether 'close contact' refers to emotional support, a confidant(e) or practical assistance. It is also impossible to distinguish between 'everyday' social support (Weiss, 1974) and 'crisis' support (Cobb, 1976), which may be perceived and recalled differently by the individual (O'Reilly, 1988). To place social support into a real-life context, other researchers have used questionnaires to describe a hypothetical situation and then ask respondents to indicate whether or not support would be available in that situation, and if so, by whom.

In addition to perceived social support, an alternative is to measure actual or 'received' social support or the extent of social interaction. From HALS we have derived a measure based on reported contact with friends and family over the two weeks preceding the survey. Respondents were asked separately about friends and relatives in terms of whether or not they had any of the following four types of contact: went to visit them, went out with them, spoke on the telephone or received visits. Responses to these four items were scored and used to create two indicators: *actual contact with relatives* and *actual contact with friends* (see Appendix A). Using these two scales we can distinguish between those with little or no contact over the two-week period, some contact (2–3 types) or maximum contact across all four types. The main limitation of these measures is that we are forced to rely on the assumption that greater contact with friends and family will be positively related to social support. In addition it is likely that the items scored on these scales will be influenced by geographical proximity to friends and relatives.

Having a chronic illness which impairs mobility may reduce the amount of contact with friends and relatives. However, a severe illness or disability may increase contact with relatives who are providing emotional and/or practical support. We are only able to establish whether or not a contact was made with friends or relatives over a two-week period and have no information about frequency of each of the four types of contact. It is therefore possible that someone may speak to geographically distant relatives on the telephone every day, but still score only 1 on the actual contact with relatives scale.

The social correlates of social support

Table 5.2 shows how our three measures of social support: perceived close contact with friends and relatives; actual contact with friends and actual contact with relatives vary according to age for men and women. Women are more likely than men to report that they have close friends and relatives that they see on a regular basis, but there is little variation according to age. The proportion who have the maximum of 4 types of contact with friends over a two-week period decreases with increasing age for men and women, whilst actual contact with relatives does not vary by age for either sex.

Studies have shown that social support, as measured by a supportive and understanding confidant(e), is more likely to be available to married rather than single people (Ross and Mirowsky, 1989). Women reportedly develop more intensive social attachments than men (Belle, 1987), and there is some evidence that men are more likely to benefit from supportive relationships within marriage than women (Umberson, 1992; Cramer, 1993).

Figure 5.5 shows how perceived close contact with friends and relatives differs for men and women according to their marital status. Men who are divorced are slightly less likely to say they have both close friends and relatives than married or single men, but comparable proportions of widowed, divorced and married men report having close relatives only. For both sexes, the single and divorced are most likely to report close friends only (rather than close relatives), which could suggest that close relationships for the married are more likely to be centred around home and family ties. For men and women who are widowed, contact with close friends (and not close relatives) remains at a low level similar to that for the married, and there is some evidence that widowers are more likely to be socially isolated from contact with close friends and relatives.

As discussed earlier, the length of time living in an area may relate to the degree of social integration, which in turn is linked to social capital. The degree of integration into a community may also influence the availability or receipt of social support. Figure 5.6 shows that length of residence is significantly associated with having both close friends and relatives. Men and women who have lived in an area for one year or less are less likely to have contact with both close friends and relatives than longer term residents. This could suggest that residential mobility disrupts or impairs social support received from an established social network. However, our results show that short-term residents are most likely to have close contact either only with relatives or only with close friends. They are more likely to lack contact with either friends or relatives.

Table 5.2. Social support from friends and relatives by age group: men and women aged 16–74 years

	Men				Women			
	16–34	35–54	55–74	All 16–74	16–34	35–54	55–74	All 16–74
(a) Perceived close contact with friends and relatives								
Both close friends and relatives	74	71	75	73	80	79	78	79
Close relatives only	12	16	16	14	7	11	12	10
Close friends only	11	9	5	9	10	8	3	2
No close friends or relatives	4	5	5	5	2	3	3	2
%	100	100	100	100	100	100	100	100
N =	1015	862	607	2484	982	863	676	2621
(b) Actual contact with friends in last 2 weeks								
4 types of contact	45	22	20	31	40	26	22	30
2–3 types of contact	33	39	32	34	38	42	35	39
0–1 type of contact	22	39	49	35	22	32	44	31
%	100	100	100	100	100	100	100	100
N =	1015	862	608	2485	981	863	676	2620
(c) Actual contact with relatives in last 2 weeks								
4 types of contact	20	19	18	19	23	22	22	22
2–3 types of contact	44	48	49	46	50	50	51	51
0–1 type of contact	37	34	35	35	27	28	27	27
%	100	100	100	100	100	100	100	100
N =	1015	864	607	2486	981	863	675	2519

(a) $P < 0.01$ for men and women; (b) $P < 0.001$ for men and women; (c) P (ns) for men and women.
Source: HEA Health and Lifestyles Survey, 1992

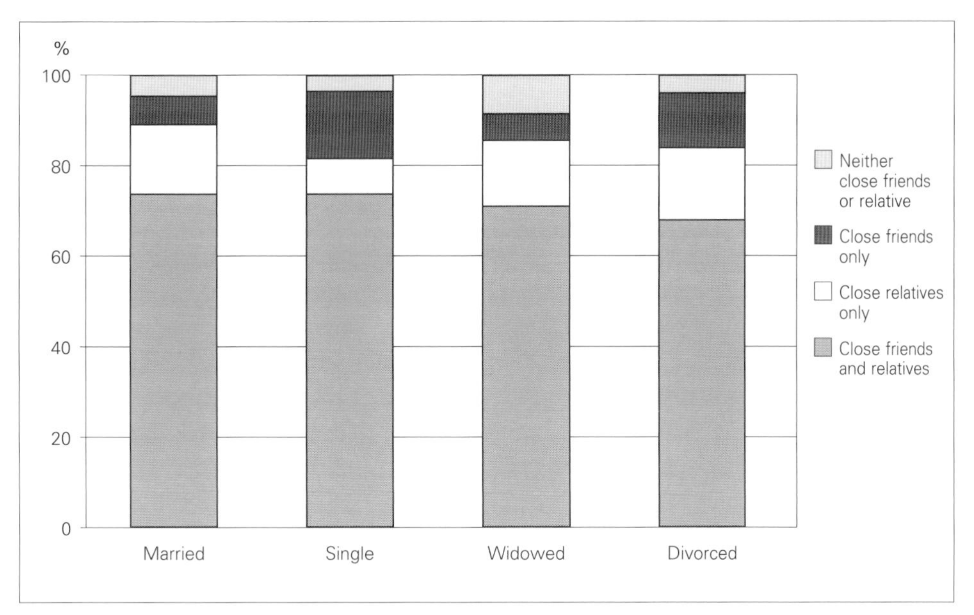

Men
$P < 0.001$

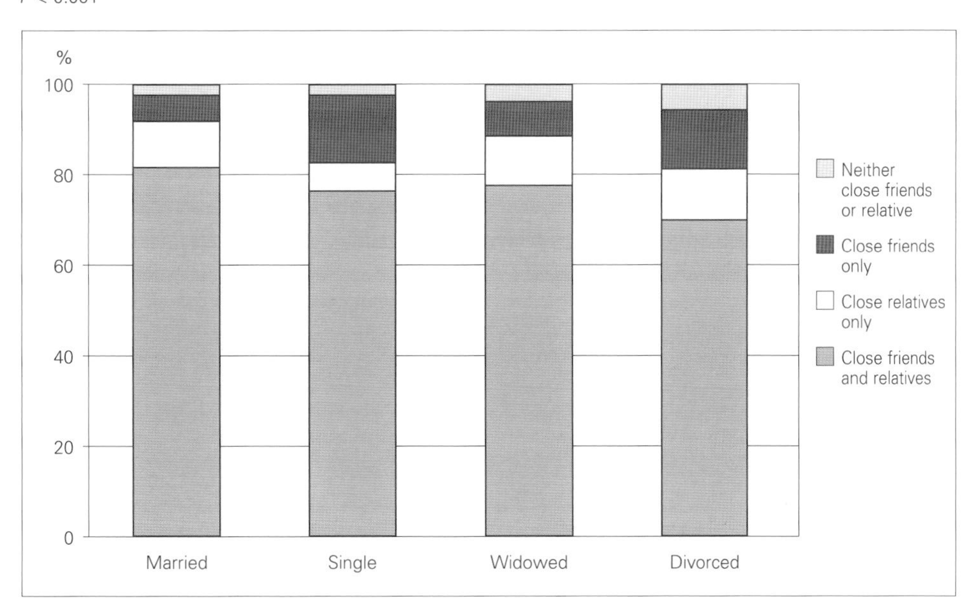

Women
$P < 0.001$
Source: HEA Health and Lifestyles Survey, 1992

Fig. 5.5.* Perceived close contact with friends and relatives by marital status: men and women aged 16–74 years

*Actual percentages are shown in tables in Appendix E.

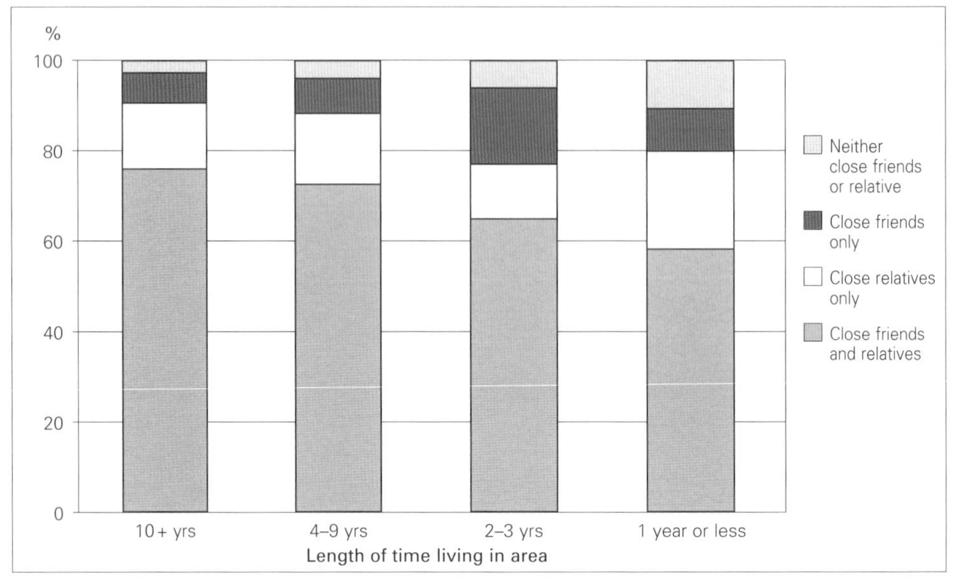

Men $P < 0.001$

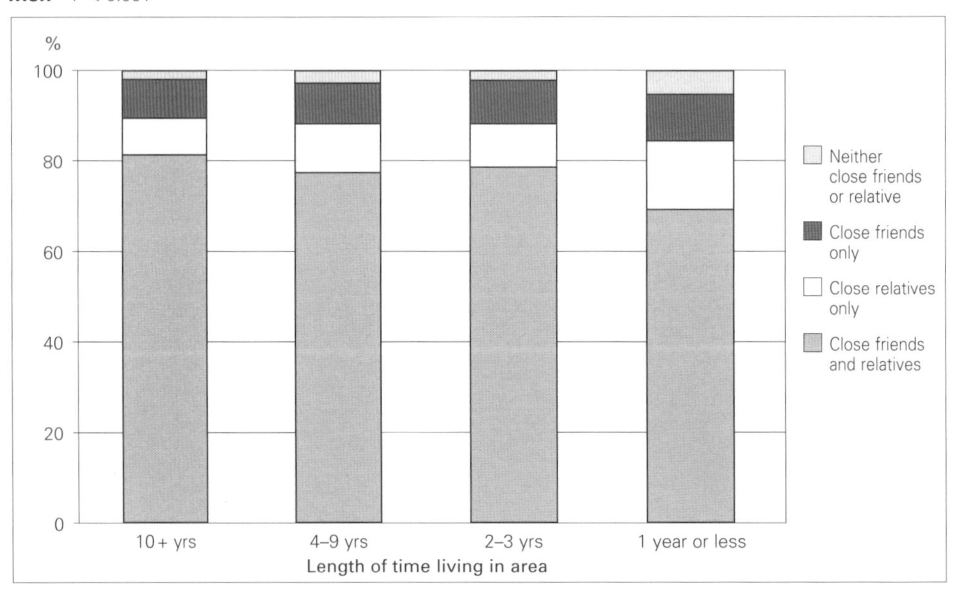

Women $P < 0.01$

Source: HEA Health and Lifestyles Survey, 1992

Fig. 5.6. **Perceived close contact with friends and relatives by length of time living in area: men and women aged 16–74 years***

*Actual percentages shown in tables in Appendix E.

Structure of Part II

Access to a supportive social network has been shown to be positively related to the physical and mental health of individuals (see Part I) whilst low levels of social capital are associated with poor self-assessed health (Kawachi, Kennedy and Lochner, 1997). The presence of social support and social capital may serve to bolster self-esteem or protect the individual against the presumed damaging effects of stress on health. Chapter 6 considers the pattern of these relationships in detail using data from the HEA Health and Lifestyles Survey. Measures of social capital and social support are related to reported stress, self-assessed health and chronic illness for men and women aged 16–74 years after accounting for socioeconomic differences in stress and health status. We also consider whether any positive association between social support or social capital and self-assessed health is mediated by stress.

Social support and social capital may benefit health indirectly by influencing health behaviour. Chapter 7 includes the analysis of two health-related behaviours: smoking and diet. Results are primarily based on data from the Health Survey for England but results are also presented for smoking and social capital based on the HEA Health and Lifestyle Survey. This chapter examines whether quality of diet and cigarette smoking vary according to perceived social support from friends and relatives after controlling for structural factors, such as social class and material deprivation, that are known to be strongly associated with these health behaviours.

In Chapter 8 we focus on the health and health behaviour of older people aged 65 and above using data from the General Household Survey. Social support measures are based on reported frequency of contact with neighbours, friends and relatives. We investigate whether the association between these measures and self-assessed health and smoking behaviour can be accounted for by structural factors or functional disability in later life.

Chapter 9 draws conclusions about, firstly, the ways in which social capital and social support themselves vary according to age, gender and social characteristics and, secondly, how these influence the health status, reported stress, diet and smoking behaviour of men and women in different ways. Thirdly, it highlights the relative importance of structural factors, social capital and social support in determining health and health behaviour.

6. Relating social capital and social support to health status and reported stress

How social capital and social support relate to the health of individuals from different socioeconomic backgrounds has been the subject of little large-scale research in Britain. Chapter 5 demonstrated how these concepts could be quantified using data from the 1992 Health and Lifestyles Survey (HALS) (HEA, 1995) and the potential limitations of these measures. In this chapter we investigate how levels of social support and social capital are associated with self-assessed health, limiting long-standing illness and reported levels of stress among men and women aged 16–74 years. The relative influence of social support and social capital is compared to structural indicators of material living circumstances, social class and employment status. Details of all the variables used in this analysis are included in Appendix A.

Socioeconomic position, perceived stress and health status

We use four indicators to capture different dimensions of an individual's socioeconomic position and material living environment. Our analysis includes the individual's occupational social class, their highest educational qualification, current employment status and a scored index of 'personal deprivation'. The latter measure is based on the material resources available to each individual in their household, such as central heating and car ownership. Details about how this scale was constructed are given in Appendix A.

The HALS data include the respondent's assessment of the amount of stress they have experienced over the preceding 12 months. We focus on those who report large amounts of stress, but it is possible that such stress can be positive as well as negative depending on its meaning to the individual concerned (Turner and Avison, 1992).

Figure 6.1 shows a significant relationship between occupational social class and stress for men and women aged 16–74 years. Women currently employed in the highest social class are substantially more likely to report a large amount of stress compared with men in this class and with women in other classes. For men, stress is greatest in class II and then consistently decreases in the manual social classes. These findings are likely to reflect the work-related stress of those employed in professional occupations, particularly women, with lower occupational groups generally reporting lower levels of stress. Relatively high levels of stress are reported by the unclassified group, which in HALS includes those who are not currently in employment; 20% of men and 24% of women in this group report large amounts of stress.

Women who are divorced are more than twice as likely to report high stress as single, married or widowed women (Figure 6.2). Marital dissolution is also associated with greater stress for men, with married and single men reporting the least stress over the last year. It is impossible to tell from this cross-sectional survey data whether high levels of stress contribute to marital breakdown, or whether the loss of a spouse through death or divorce is responsible for the raised levels of reported stress.

Health status is measured according to whether the respondent has a limiting long-standing illness (LLI) or rates their general health as less than very good (see Appendix A). The likelihood of having LLI or poor general health has been shown to be greater among the lower socioeconomic groups than among those who are more advantaged (Townsend, Phillimore and Beattie, 1988; Arber, 1997). Table 6.1 shows a strong association between material deprivation (as measured by the personal deprivation index – PDI) and LLI for men and women. For all age groups, those living in the most materially deprived conditions (PDI score 3+) are more likely to have a chronic illness than those with a PDI score of 0, and this is particularly marked for men aged 35–54 and older women aged 55–74 years.

Relating social capital and social support to reported health status and stress

We begin by analysing the relationship between social capital, reported health status and stress, to consider whether individuals with low social capital are more likely to report poorer health and greater stress than those with high social capital.

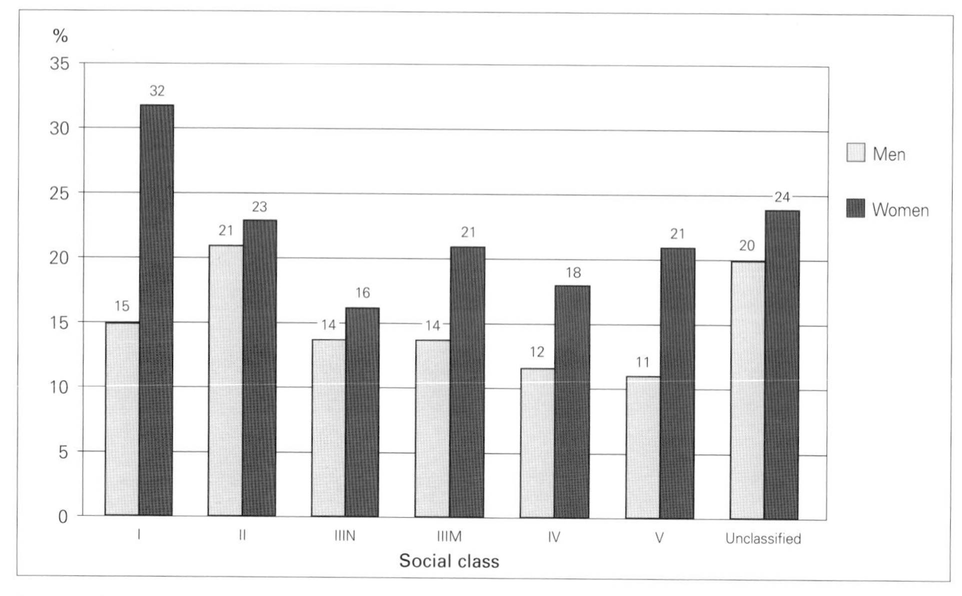

$P < 0.001$ for men and women

Source: HEA Health and Lifestyles Survey, 1992

Fig. 6.1. **Percentage reporting large amounts of stress by social class: men and women aged 16–74 years**

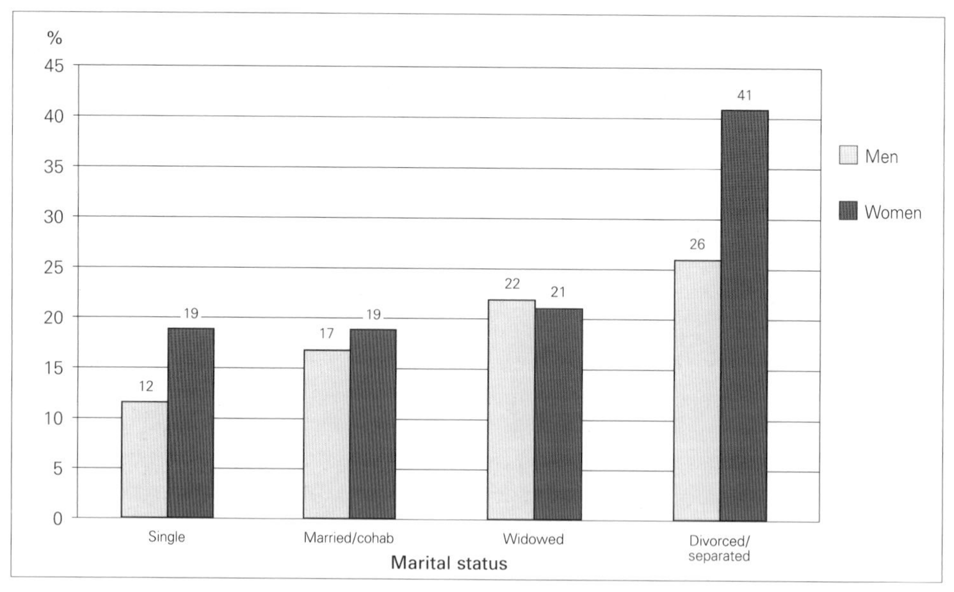

$P < 0.001$ for men and women

Source: HEA Health and Lifestyles Survey, 1992

Fig. 6.2. **Percentage reporting large amounts of stress by marital status: men and women aged 16–74 years**

Table 6.1. Percentage reporting limiting long-standing illness by personal deprivation (PDI) score: men and women aged 16–74 years

	PDI score					
	0	1	2	3+	All	*P* (Sig)
(a) Men						
16–34	5	6	9	13	7	< 0.05
N =	(428)	(277)	(147)	(106)	(958)	
35–54	10	10	15	29	12	< 0.001
N =	(538)	(141)	(62)	(60)	(802)	
55–74	23	40	34	37	30	< 0.01
N =	(312)	(120)	(57)	(69)	(558)	
All aged 16–74	11	15	16	24	14	< 0.001
N =	(1278)	(540)	(266)	(235)	(2319)	
(b) Women						
16–34	6	10	9	16	9	< 0.01
N =	(75)	(238)	(132)	(150)	(894)	
35–54	14	20	25	22	17	< 0.05
N =	(493)	(143)	(74)	(73)	(784)	
55–74	21	32	29	42	27	< 0.01
N =	(293)	(158)	(103)	(64)	(618)	
All aged 16–74	13	19	20	23	17	< 0.001
N =	(1160)	(539)	(309)	(287)	(2296)	

Source: HEA Health and Lifestyles Survey, 1992

Figure 6.3 shows how the measure of neighbourhood social capital derived from the HALS is associated with having a limiting long-standing illness, reporting that general health is less than very good and reporting high levels of stress over the last year. For men, there is no clear evidence that a low level of neighbourhood social capital is associated with greater stress, but some evidence that men with a very high level of neighbourhood social capital are more likely to report very good general health than those with low social capital. For women, very high social capital is significantly associated with good general health. Approximately half of women with very high neighbourhood social capital report that their general health is very good, which decreases to 43% among those with low social capital. Women with a low neighbourhood social capital score are also significantly more likely to report high stress and limiting long-standing illness compared with those who have very high social capital, whereas for men there is no statistically significant relationship between social capital and the three health measures. Our results suggest that the relationship between neighbourhood social capital and health is gendered, with women's health being adversely affected by a poor social and living environment, but this is less evident for men.

Similarly there is a significant positive relationship between general health and community activity for women but not for men (Table 6.2). Of women who were active in the community 52% reported very good health, but among those who were not involved in

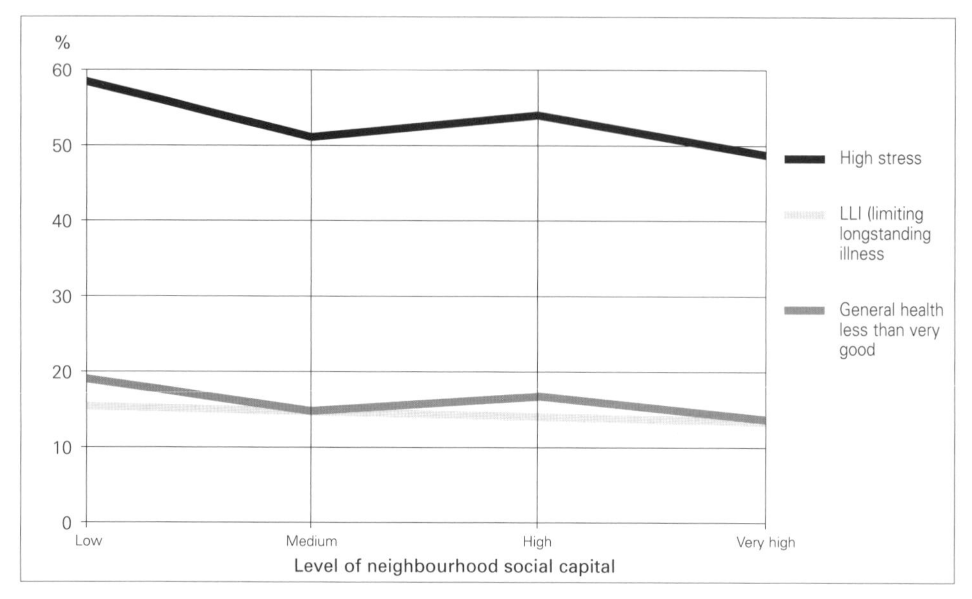

Men

Stress P (ns); general health $P < 0.05$; LLI P (ns)

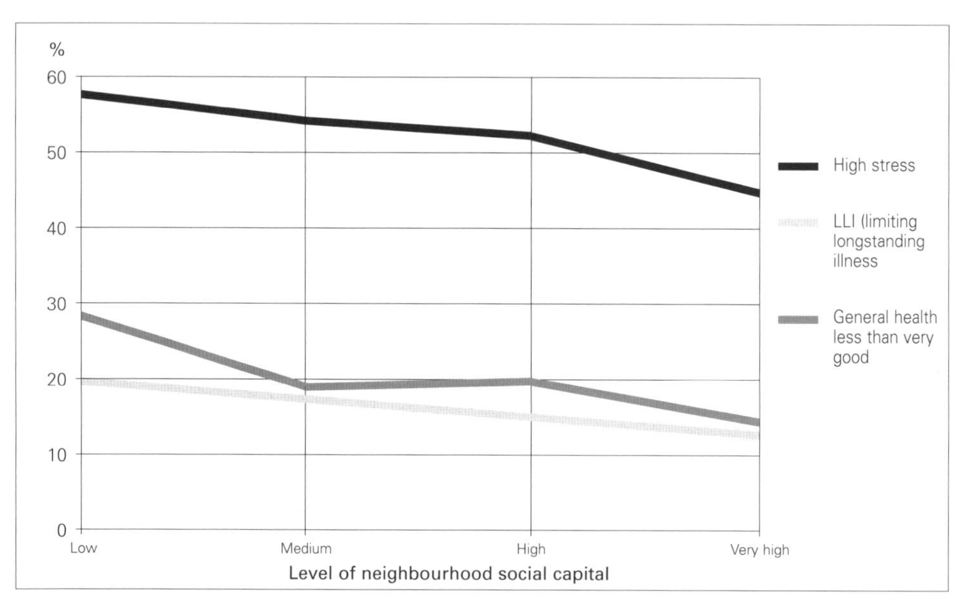

Women

Stress P (ns); general health $P < 0.05$; LLI P (ns)

Source: HEA Health and Lifestyles Survey, 1992

Fig. 6.3.* Neighbourhood social capital and health status: men and women aged 16–74 years

*Actual percentages are shown in Appendix E.

Table 6.2. Percentage reporting very good health by community activity: men and women aged 16–74 years

	Men			Women		
	Community activity	No community activity	All	Community activity	No community activity	All
General health						
Very good	50	46	47	52	45	47
Fairly good	45	46	46	43	46	45
Fairly poor	4	6	6	4	7	6
Very poor	1	2	2	1	2	2
%	100	100	100	100	100	100
N =	438	2039	2477	628	1879	2507

Men P (ns); Women $P < 0.01$
Source: HEA Health and Lifestyles Survey, 1992

Table 6.3. Levels of stress according to whether victim of crime or attack in last year: men and women aged 16–74 years

	Men			Women		
	Not victim	Victim of crime and/or attack	All	Not victim	Victim of crime and/or attack	All
No stress	19	4	17	16	3	14
Small amount	34	34	34	35	29	35
Moderate amount	31	42	33	30	36	30
Large amount	15	21	16	20	31	21
%	100	100	100	100	100	100
N =	2135	334	2468	2252	252	2504

$P < 0.001$ for men and women
Source: HEA Health and Lifestyles Survey, 1992

community activity the proportion was only 45%. For men, a greater proportion of those involved in community activity reported very good health, but this was only slightly reduced among non-active men. A small proportion of men and women
rated their health as very poor and this was slightly greater among the non-active groups. However, there is likely to be a reciprocal causal relationship between community participation and health; community activity may promote good health and poor health may limit the extent to which an individual is able to participate in community activities.

An experience of crime or attack in the last year is strongly associated with stress for both men and women (Table 6.3). Nearly one-third of these women and 20% of men report a large amount of stress compared with 20% of women and 15% of men who have not been the victim of crime or attack in the last year. Women are more likely than men to report a large amount of stress regardless of whether they have been a victim of crime, with men more likely to report no stress at all in the last year.

Table 6.4. Percentage of men and women reporting very good health by age and social support from friends and relatives

	Men				Women			
	16–34	**35–54**	**55–74**	**All 16–74**	**16–34**	**35–54**	**55–74**	**All 16–74**
(a) Perceived close contact with friends and relatives								
Both close friends and relatives	47 (746)	50 (606)	44 (451)	47 (1805)	50 (787)	54 (675)	41 (529)	49 (1991)
Close relatives only	49 (117)	49 (134)	40 (94)	46 (346)	44 (73)	41 (91)	38 (81)	41 (245)
Close friends only	47 (109)	48 (78)	35 (27)	46 (214)	43 (100)	40 (66)	47 (48)	43 (213)
No close friends or relatives	41 (43)	43 (40)	20 (28)	36 (111)	34 (19)	36 (22)	41 (17)	37 (57)
P (Sig)	ns	ns	ns	ns	ns	< 0.05	ns	< 0.05
(b) Actual contact with friends in last 2 weeks								
4 contacts	50 (460)	51 (192)	50 (120)	50 (772)	52 (338)	57 (222)	51 (144)	53 (754)
2–3 contacts	45 (330)	52 (330)	43 (190)	47 (853)	47 (376)	54 (361)	43 (236)	49 (972)
0–1 contact	45 (225)	44 (336)	39 (291)	43 (852)	44 (215)	42 (271)	34 (294)	39 (780)
P (Sig)	ns	ns	ns	< 0.05	ns	< 0.01	< 0.01	< 0.001
(c) Actual contact with relatives in last 2 weeks								
4 contacts	45 (202)	52 (162)	49 (107)	48 (471)	52 (229)	52 (188)	43 (145)	50 (563)
2–3 contacts	48 (443)	47 (407)	42 (288)	46 (1140)	48 (490)	53 (429)	36 (345)	46 (1263)
0–1 contact	48 (370)	49 (290)	40 (205)	47 (866)	47 (259)	46 (238)	47 (184)	47 (681)
P (Sig)	ns	ns	ns	ns	ns	ns	ns	ns

ns = not statistically significant at $P < 0.05$ level
Base numbers are given in brackets
Source: HEA Health and Lifestyles Survey, 1992

Previous research suggests that social support can have a positive influence on health and wellbeing, for example, a significant other may care for an individual's health needs or encourage lifestyle behaviours that promote better health. Table 6.4 shows how the HALS measures of perceived and received social support are related to whether men and women report very good general health. For men in all age groups and women aged between 16 and 54, those without close friends or relatives are less likely to report very good health than those who report having both close friends and relatives (Table 6.4(a)). For men in all age groups there is little difference between those reporting close friends and relatives and those in close contact with friends or relatives only. However, only 36% of men with no close friends or relatives rate their health as 'very good' compared with 47% with both close friends and relatives. For women, there is more variation in the reported health status of those with close friends and/or relatives. Over half of women aged 35–54 with close friends and relatives report very good general health, but this falls to approximately 40% among women in close contact with only one of these groups and is lowest at 36% for women without close friends or relatives.

Friends seem to be more important for good health than relatives (Table 6.4(b)). Increasing contact with friends is positively related to general health, with over half of men and women aged 16–74 years reporting very good health when they have the maximum of four types of contact with friends over a two-week period compared with 43% of men and 39% of women who have little or no contact during this time period. This difference is especially marked for older men and women where the proportion reporting very good health is consistently reduced as contact with friends becomes more infrequent.

The relationship between contact with relatives and health is more inconsistent and does not reach statistical significance. The greatest proportion of men aged 16–34 and older women aged 55–74 report very good health when there is little or no contact with relatives (Table 6.4(c)). However, in some age groups there is a suggestion that frequent contact with relatives is positively related to health status, particularly for older men. Overall our results suggest that actual contact with friends is more strongly associated with self-assessed health than contact with relatives over a short time period of two weeks.

Although our results indicate that social support is positively related to health, it is likely that health status itself will have different and opposing influences on the type and amount of social support received. For example, having a limiting long-standing illness or disability may reduce visiting and outside social activities with friends and relatives, but increase home visits by relatives who may provide practical support.

Summary

The measures of social capital and social support from the HALS data were significantly associated with reported health status and stress. High neighbourhood social capital and contact with friends and relatives were associated with better health outcomes and reduced stress, especially for women. Older age groups were most likely to have high social capital and greater community participation and women's health was more strongly associated with these social factors than for men. For both sexes, a high number of contacts with friends was positively related to general health, whereas actual contact with relatives was not significantly associated with health status. However, social capital and social support themselves vary according to an individual's socioeconomic position; being unemployed was associated with low neighbourhood social capital and less community participation, whilst marital status influenced the amount of contact with friends and relatives. Numerous research studies have shown that socioeconomic characteristics are associated with reported health and stress for both sexes (Townsend, Phillimore and Beattie, 1988; McLeod and Kessler, 1990), although the structural position of men and women may differ (Arber, 1997; Arber and Cooper, 1999).

It is therefore important to control for age, sex and socioeconomic characteristics in order to examine the relative influence of social capital and social support on health status. We examine three measures of health: the reporting of less than very good general health, limiting long-standing illness and high levels of stress, using multivariate logistic regression analysis (see Appendix D). Separate models are computed for men and women to highlight any gender differences in the effects of social capital and social support on reported health and stress after adjusting for any variation associated with their socioeconomic position.

Multivariate analysis

We use three outcome measures: Table 6.5 shows the odds of reporting large amounts of stress over the last year, Table 6.6 presents the odds of reporting less than very good general health, and the odds of having a limiting long-standing illness (LLI) are given in Table 6.7. Two logistic models are presented in each table; the first includes age, marital status and indicators of socioeconomic position, and the second adds all social capital and social support measures to examine their association with health and stress after adjusting for age and socioeconomic variation. In each of these tables, only the overall 'best fit' model is presented (see Appendix D). The results are given separately for men and women to illustrate any gender differences in the factors associated with health and stress.

Reported stress for men and women aged 16–74 years

Model 1 (Table 6.5) shows that age is more strongly associated with reported high levels of stress for women than for men. Women aged 35–44 and 45–54 have higher levels of stress than the youngest age group (the reference category); their odds ratio of stress increased by 86% and 62% respectively compared to women aged 16–24 years, which may relate to stresses associated with the main years of family formation and paid employment. The youngest age group of men (16–24 years) are most likely to report large amounts of stress, with older men aged 65–74 years having significantly lower stress than this group.

Marital status is strongly associated with stress, but differently for men and women. Single men are significantly less likely to report large amounts of stress relative to married men, whereas the odds ratio of stress for single women is comparable to the reference category (the married or cohabiting). Divorced women have an odds ratio of over two of reporting large amounts of stress compared to their married counterparts, after controlling for age and socioeconomic factors in the model. The odds ratios of stress are increased for men and women who are widowed, but do not reach statistical significance.

As shown in Figure 6.1, women currently employed in the highest social class occupations are more likely than any other social class to report large amounts of stress, with some evidence that men in class II have an increased likelihood of reporting stress. Among those groups that are not currently employed and are therefore excluded from the occupational social classes, the sick and disabled are more likely to report stress than class I, although this is only statistically significant for men.

For both sexes, the odds ratio of reporting large amounts of stress increases with material deprivation. Among those living in the most materially deprived conditions (PDI score of 3+), the odds of high stress are increased by 94% for men and 67% for women compared with those with a PDI score of 0. The finding that the highest social classes and most materially disadvantaged have the greatest reported stress could indicate two different types of stress: work-related stress and stress associated with a lack of material resources. These could have different consequences for health and wellbeing.

Three of the four measures of social capital were selected into the final model (Model 2), but none of the measures of social support reached statistical significance after controlling for the other factors in the model. The three social capital measures significantly improved the fit of the model for women but none reached statistical significance for men. The odds ratios are presented for both sexes in Table 6.5 to facilitate comparison between men and

Table 6.5. Odds ratios for experiencing large amounts of stress: men and women aged 16–74 years

	Men		Women	
	Model 1	Model 2	Model 1	Model 2
Age	†	ns	†††	†††
16–24	1.00	1.00	1.00	1.00
25–34	0.97	0.96	1.35	1.51
35–44	0.90	0.99	1.86**	2.26***
45–54	0.90	1.02	1.62*	1.91**
55–64	0.63	0.75	0.99	1.29
65–74	0.42**	0.50*	0.63	0.85
Marital status	††	††	†††	†††
Married/cohabiting	1.00	1.00	1.00	1.00
Single	0.60**	0.65*	1.06	1.18
Widowed	1.90	1.98	1.38	1.41
Divorced/separated	1.57	1.54	2.32***	2.37***
Social class	†††	†††	††	††
I	1.00	1.00	1.00	1.00
II	1.45	1.45	0.69	0.72
IIIN	0.93	0.95	0.41	0.45
IIIM	0.79	0.82	0.66	0.73
IV/V	0.68	0.71	0.48	0.51
Long-term unemployed	1.10	1.18	0.55	0.59
In education/training	0.74	0.74	0.63	0.66
Sick/disabled	2.25*	2.24*	1.33	1.59
At home	1.99	2.11	0.67	0.74
PDI score	†	†	†	ns
0	1.00	1.00	1.00	1.00
1	1.07	1.04	1.10	0.99
2	1.45	1.32	1.41	1.23
3+	1.94**	1.79**	1.67**	1.29
Neighbourhood social capital		ns		†††
Very high		1.00		1.00
High		1.32		1.45*
Medium		1.27		1.47*
Low		1.35		2.41***
Whether victim of crime or attack		ns		†
No		1.00		1.00
Yes		1.36		1.50*
Length of time living in area		ns		†
10+ years		1.00		1.00
4–9 years		1.15		0.97
2–3 years		1.27		1.23
1 year or less		1.53*		1.74**
N =	1906	1906	2444	2444
Δ LLR	78.7	11.8	106.5	45.4
Δ df	19	7	19	7

Significance of difference from reference category: *$P < 0.05$; **$P < 0.01$; *** $P < 0.001$

Significance of variable in the model: †$P < 0.05$; ††$P < 0.01$; †††$P < 0.001$.

Variables not statistically significant in the final model; educational level, employment status, involvement with friends, kin involvement, close contact with friends/relatives, community activity.

Source: HEA Health and Lifestyles Survey, 1992

women and to show that social capital influences stress for women only. The overall contribution of social capital measures to the fit of the model is much less than for the socioeconomic factors entered in Model 1, and is shown by the change in LLR for men and women (see Appendix D).

There is a significant inverse association between neighbourhood social capital and stress for women. Women with low neighbourhood social capital have an odds ratio more than twice as high of reporting large amounts of stress relative to women whose level of social capital is very high. The odds ratio of stress is increased for men with low social capital, but does not vary significantly from the reference category.

Being the victim of crime or attack is significantly associated with stress for women but not for men after controlling for material deprivation and social class in the model. Being resident in an area for one year or less is associated with greater stress for both sexes relative to long-term residents of 10 or more years, but this variable only reaches overall statistical significance for women.

Adding measures of social capital to the model does little to alter the association between socioeconomic position and stress for men, with materially deprived and sick/disabled men most likely to report large amounts of stress, and stress is significantly lower for single and older men. Women aged between 35 and 54 years remain most likely to report large amounts of stress, along with divorced/separated women, but personal deprivation is no longer a significant predictor of stress. This could suggest that differential levels of social capital in the area of residence can explain at least part of the association between structural disadvantage and stress for women. Women living in the most materially deprived circumstances also tend to live in areas with lower neighbourhood social capital, and negative perceptions of their living environment and community may contribute to their greater levels of reported stress.

Limiting long-standing illness (LLI) for men and women 16–74 years

There is a strong association between age and reporting limiting long-standing illness. Table 6.6 shows that 16–24-year-old men and women are least likely to have a chronic illness, with the highest odds of LLI found for those aged 45–54 years relative to this group (Model 1), after controlling for employment status and PDI in the model.

The only two measures of socioeconomic position which were significantly associated with LLI were employment status and the PDI measure of material deprivation; social

Table 6.6. Odds ratios of limiting long-standing illness: men and women aged 16–74 years

	Men		Women	
	Model 1	Model 2	Model 1	Model 2
Age	†††	†††	†††	†††
16–24	1.00	1.00	1.00	1.00
25–34	3.52***	3.37***	1.09	1.10
35–44	3.59***	3.26***	1.94**	1.91**
45–54	8.04***	7.09***	4.41***	3.95***
55–64	7.59***	6.71***	3.34***	3.34***
65–74	4.32***	3.66***	2.54***	2.49***
Employment status	†††	†††	†††	†††
Work full time	1.00	1.00	1.00	1.00
Work part time	3.55***	3.53***	1.09	1.12
Unemployed	1.89**	1.86*	2.45**	2.42**
Non-employed	6.89***	7.25***	3.14***	3.21***
PDI score	††	†	††	†
0	1.00	1.00	1.00	1.00
1	1.43*	1.39*	1.62**	1.50**
2	1.59*	1.46	1.47*	1.31
3+	2.17***	1.90**	1.83***	1.49*
Neighbourhood social capital		ns		††
Very high		1.00		1.00
High		0.93		1.27
Medium		1.23		1.59*
Low		1.27		1.94***
Contact with friends		†		ns
4 contacts		1.00		1.00
2–3 contacts		1.34		1.06
0–1 contact		1.64**		1.35
N =	2004	2004	2552	2552
Δ LLR	304.0	12.2	194.9	19.9
Δ df	11	5	11	5

Significance of difference from reference category: **P* < 0.05; ***P* < 0.01; *** *P* < 0.001
Significance of variable in the model: †*P* < 0.05; ††*P* < 0.01; †††*P* < 0.001
Variables not statistically significant in the final model: marital status, social class, educational level, kin involvement, community activity, close contact with friends and/or relatives, length of time living in area, whether victim of crime or attack
Source: HEA Health and Lifestyles Survey, 1992

class did not have a significant effect (Model 1). Full-time workers are least likely to have a chronic illness, with an odds ratio of over six for non-employed men and over three for non-employed women compared to those employed full time. Being unemployed is also significantly associated with having a limiting long-standing illness for both sexes, and men working part time have a more than three times higher odds ratio than those employed full time. Women working full time and part time have similar low levels of LLI. These results are likely to represent a 'healthy worker' effect (Sterling and Weinkam, 1985), with only the healthiest men and women being selected into paid employment and retained by the labour force.

After controlling for employment status and age, material deprivation is significantly associated with the likelihood of LLI (Model 1). For men there is a linear increase in the odds ratio of LLI as material deprivation increases, with men living in the most materially deprived conditions having an odds ratio more than two times higher of reporting LLI than those with no derivation on our PDI scale. Women who are not materially deprived (PDI score 0) are also least likely to have a chronic illness, with the odds ratio increased by 83% for the most materially deprived.

When social capital and social support measures are added (Model 2), neighbourhood social capital is significantly associated with LLI for women but not men, whereas contact with friends is statistically significant in the model for men only. Women with a medium or low level of neighbourhood social capital have their odds ratio of LLI significantly increased by 59% and 94% respectively compared to women with very high neighbourhood social capital after controlling for the other variables in the model. This contrasts with men where low neighbourhood social capital is not significantly different from the reference category and overall neighbourhood social capital does not make any significant contribution to the model. However, men who had little contact with friends over a two-week period (0–1 types of contact) are significantly more likely to have a reported chronic illness than those with the maximum of four types of contact during this time (Model 2). For women, involvement with friends is not significantly associated with their chronic health status after controlling for their level of social capital and socioeconomic position, although the odds ratio of LLI is higher (1.35) for women with minimal contact compared to the reference category of four types of contact.

The overall influence of social capital and social support measures on limiting long-standing illness in these logistic models is much lower than for socioeconomic factors. However, the addition of these variables in Model 2 weakens the association between material deprivation and LLI, although the odds ratio is still significantly increased by 90% among men and 49% among women who are most deprived. This could suggest that some of the adverse effects of living in poor material circumstances on health are related to neighbourhood social capital and contact with friends.

One explanation for these findings is that individuals who are materially deprived are also more likely to report living in a neighbourhood with a low level of social capital, and this is associated with chronic ill health – particularly for women. However, it is also likely that community resources, such as transport and leisure (both of which are included in our social capital measure) may be more unsatisfactory for those with LLI than for those with no chronic illness, due to restricted mobility, for example. Similarly, social support gained from contact with friends (but not relatives) may be made more problematic for those with LLI, and decreased contact, particularly for men, may contribute to greater feelings of social isolation and lower social capital.

The association between employment status and LLI is not weakened by controlling for social capital and social support, with the odds ratios of LLI greater for the non-employed in Model 2 than in Model 1. The non-employed group includes the long-term sick and retired, both of whom will have higher than average levels of LLI.

Very good general health for men and women 16–74 years

There is little difference in the reporting of very good general health for men of different ages, and for women there is a curved relationship with better health reported by women aged 35–44 years (Model 1). Men aged 16–24 are most likely to report very good general health, with the oldest age group of men and women aged 65–74 being significantly more likely to report their general health as being less than very good relative to the reference category of 16–24-year-olds (Table 6.7; Model 1), after social class and material deprivation are included in the model.

General health status is strongly associated with social class (Model 1), with men in class I most likely to report very good health. The odds ratio of less than very good health is more than doubled for those in social class IIIN, the long-term unemployed and those in full-time education, and substantially increased for those employed in manual occupations (classes IIIM to V) relative to social class I. Women in social classes I and II are most likely to report very good general health, but although the odds ratio shows poorer health in lower social classes, the likelihood of poor general health is not significantly different from class I. Women who are long-term unemployed are significantly more likely to rate their health as less than very good and, as expected, being sick/disabled is strongly associated with poor subjective health for men and women.

After controlling for social class and age, material deprivation was not significantly associated with general health for men, but the odds ratio of less than very good general health was significantly increased for women with a PDI score of 1 or more (Model 1). Overall, adding age and these two measures of socioeconomic position substantially improves the overall fit of the model (as shown by the Log Likelihood Ratio) by 90.7 for men and 143.0 for women.

Table 6.7. Odds ratios of less than very good general health: men and women aged 16–74 years

	Men			Women		
	Model 1	Model 2	Model 3	Model 1	Model 2	Model 3
Age	ns	ns	†	†††	††	†††
16–24	1.00	1.00	1.00	1.00	1.00	1.00
25–34	1.19	1.16	1.08	0.74	0.74	0.67*
35–44	1.14	1.07	0.93	0.72*	0.69*	0.61**
45–54	1.19	1.09	1.03	0.95	0.89	0.86
55–64	1.10	1.04	1.04	1.01	0.97	0.99
65–74	1.69**	1.57*	1.69**	1.45*	1.33	1.61*
Social class	†††	†††	†††	†††	†††	†††
I	1.00	1.00	1.00	1.00	1.00	1.00
II	1.38	1.33	1.30	0.84	0.87	0.91
IIIN	2.12***	2.07**	2.14***	1.19	1.24	1.44
IIIM	1.82**	1.74**	1.95***	1.56	1.62	1.87
IV/V	1.79**	1.72*	1.97**	1.28	1.31	1.58
Long-term unemployed	2.48***	2.33**	2.57***	3.43*	3.42*	3.93*
FT education	2.81***	2.83***	3.12***	1.12	1.22	1.31
Sick/disabled	10.07***	9.70***	9.76***	7.76**	7.74**	8.37***
Looking after home or family	1.43	1.47	1.63	1.58	1.63	1.85
PDI score	ns	ns	ns	†††	††	††
0	1.00	1.00	1.00	1.00	1.00	1.00
1	1.25	1.23	1.23	1.49***	1.41**	1.43**
2	1.27	1.20	1.17	1.76***	1.62**	1.58**
3+	1.29	1.19	1.15	1.50**	1.30	1.28
Neighbourhood social capital		ns	ns		ns	ns
Very high		1.00	1.00		1.00	1.00
High		1.10	1.09		1.23	1.18
Medium		1.05	0.99		1.28	1.20
Low		1.32*	1.20		1.41*	1.25
Contact with friends		†	†		††	††
4 contacts		1.00	1.00		1.00	1.00
2–3 contacts		1.30*	1.33**		1.17	1.14
0–1 contact		1.34*	1.37**		1.49***	1.48**
Stress in last 12 months			†††			†††
None			1.00			1.00
Small amount			1.00			1.50**
Moderate amount			1.78***			2.61***
Large amount			2.00***			2.91***
N =	1939			2491		
Δ LLR	90.7	13.5	44.5	143.0	18.3	66.6
Δ df	16	5	3	16	5	3

Significance of difference from reference category: $*P < 0.05$; $**P < 0.01$; $*** P < 0.001$
Significance of variable in the model: $\dagger P < 0.05$; $\dagger\dagger P < 0.01$; $\dagger\dagger\dagger P < 0.001$.
Variables not statistically significant in the final model; marital status, educational level, employment status, whether victim of crime or attack, kin involvement, perceived close friends and relatives, length of time in area, community activity
Source: HEA Health and Lifestyles Survey, 1992

The measure of neighbourhood social capital was selected into the final model when men and women were combined in the analysis, but does not reach overall statistical significance when men and women are examined separately. However, despite this lack of statistical significance, there is a suggestion that men and women with low neighbourhood social capital are most likely to report poor health (Model 2).

Involvement with friends was the only measure of social support significantly associated with general health. The variables measuring actual contact with relatives and perceived close contact with friends and relatives were not selected into the final model. For both sexes, having the maximum of four types of contact with friends over the two-week period was positively associated with good general health (Model 2).

Adding social capital and involvement with friends in Model 2 does not alter how age and social class relate to general health. However, for women, the association between material deprivation and reported general health is weakened. As in Table 6.6, these findings suggest that the materially deprived are also more likely to lack active involvement with friends and to have a low level of neighbourhood social capital. The former may be facilitated by adequate financial or material resources, such as a car or telephone, whilst living in materially deprived household circumstances is likely to be associated with living in areas with a low level of neighbourhood social capital.

Model 3 examines whether the association of social capital and social support with self-assessed health can be accounted for by variation in the amount of stress reported by these groups. Controlling for stress improves the fit of the model by 44.5 for men and 66.6 for women, which is greater than the contribution of social capital and social support in Model 2, but substantially lower than that of age and socioeconomic variables in Model 1.

For both sexes, stress is strongly associated with subjective health after controlling for socioeconomic position, social capital and social support. Men and women reporting moderate or large amounts of stress are much more likely to report less than very good health than those with no stress over the preceding twelve months (Model 3).

Adding stress to the model does little to alter the association between social class and general health for men and women, and material deprivation remains a significant predictor of subjective health for women. However, the odds ratio of reporting less than very good health is no longer significantly increased for men and women with low social capital once stress is included in the model. Decreased social support, as measured by reduced contact with friends, is still associated with poorer general health for men and women after controlling for stress. These findings could indicate that much of the association between social capital and general health is not a direct one, but is mediated by stress. If individuals with low social capital are more likely to experience stress which is negatively related to their general health, then this lends support to the theory that high social capital can act as a 'buffer' against the adverse effects of stress on heath. However, there is no evidence that the poorer subjective health reported by those in less frequent contact with friends is related to higher levels of reported stress among this group.

Discussion and conclusions

Our analysis shows an age-related increase in social capital and community activity. There is little difference in the proportion of men and women reporting high levels of neighbourhood social capital, but women are more likely to participate in community activity than men. It is not possible to establish whether these age differences are because social capital has decreased over successive generations or whether individual perceptions about their area of residence change over the life course.

Our results confirm previous research that has established a direct association between socioeconomic position and health status, with men and women who are disadvantaged in terms of their employment status, social class and material resources most likely to have limiting long-standing illness and poorer general health (Arber, 1997). Material deprivation and social class are also associated with a high level of stress. Disadvantaged groups may be more vulnerable to certain types of stressor (McLeod and Kessler, 1990) or experience a reduced sense of control (Ross and Mirowsky, 1989).

Women who are divorced/separated report greater levels of stress than married, single or widowed women, and single men have the lowest levels of stress. We found some evidence to suggest that marital status can influence the composition of an individual's social network, with the divorced/separated and single more likely to have contact with close friends only and the married more likely to have family ties. These differences in social support between the married and non-married may account for some of the variation in health and reported stress between these groups.

Overall our analysis shows that health and levels of stress are much more strongly related to socioeconomic factors than to social capital and social support. These are themselves related to an individual's social and economic resources. However, neighbourhood social capital is independently associated with stress and health for women after controlling for socioeconomic factors. Alternative measures of social capital – namely, being the victim of crime and/or attack or living in an area for a short amount of time – are significantly related to stress for women but not for men.

For men, LLI and stress are not significantly related to social capital, but general health is poorer among those with low neighbourhood social capital. However, for both men and women there is some evidence to suggest that stress can account for part of the association between social capital and general health; low neighbourhood social capital does not significantly predict poor subjective health after adjusting for levels of reported stress.

The finding that social capital is gendered is an important one because it suggests that women's health is affected by their social environment to a greater extent than for men. For both sexes, their socioeconomic position is the main discriminator of ill health and stress.

The measures of social support were not significantly associated with stress after controlling for socioeconomic position and social capital. This suggests that having access to a social support network of friends and relatives is not fundamental to moderating or alleviating stress after adjusting for these other factors.

Contact with friends was more closely associated with self-assessed health and limiting long-standing illness than contact with relatives or the perceived closeness of these relationships. Contrary to previous research (Kessler, Price and Wortman, 1985), we found no evidence that social support, which is inferred in this study from social contact with friends and relatives, functions to 'buffer' the individual against the adverse effects of stress on health, since the association between general health and reported stress was not reduced by controlling for contact with friends. Our results support the suggestion that social support from friends is positively related to health regardless of an individual's level of stress (Barrera, 1986; Cohen and Willis, 1985), but there is no significant association between health and contact with relatives.

Overall our results highlight the importance of examining variation in health and stress within the wider context of an individual's physical and social environment, including access to material resources, employment status, neighbourhood social capital and sources of social support. Individuals who are 'socially excluded' from the labour market, who feel dissatisfied with their social environment or who lack economic resources are at greater risk of stress and of poor health. Although social support and social capital are weaker determinants of health and stress than socioeconomic factors, these measures continue to have a significant independent influence on health and reported stress, particularly for women.

7. Social factors affecting diet and smoking

Chapter 6 demonstrates that social support and social capital are related to health status, particularly for women. One explanation for this relationship is that living in a supportive locality and having a large social network promotes better health behaviour, which ultimately benefits health (Cohen, 1988). The absence of these may result in a tendency towards self-neglect and health-damaging behaviour.

This chapter uses data from the Health Survey for England (HSE) to examine how perceived social support from friends and relatives is associated with two health-related behaviours: quality of diet and cigarette smoking. Since this survey does not provide any information indicating social capital, we also use the HEA Health and Lifestyles Survey to investigate whether social capital (see Appendix A) influences the likelihood of smoking among those aged between 16 and 74 years.

Health behaviours have been shown to be socially patterned, with the lower socioeconomic groups most likely to smoke and least likely to eat healthy foods (Ginn, Arber and Cooper, 1999; Dowler and Calvert, 1995). However, it is not known whether low social capital or less social support from friends and relatives is positively or negatively associated with diet for men and women in different age groups. For example, a high level of social integration may foster health behaviour, encouraging an individual to lose weight or give up smoking (McBride *et al.,* 1998; Gottlieb and Green, 1984). Social support may be beneficial in buffering stress, with stress associated with an increased likelihood of smoking (Graham, 1993) and overeating (Greeno and Wing, 1994). However, there is some evidence that peer pressure may encourage negative health behaviours, such as heavy drinking and smoking (Stanton and McGee, 1996).

In this chapter, we examine the nature of the relationship between social support, social capital and health behaviour, after controlling for underlying socioeconomic variation in diet and smoking as well as other possible confounding factors, such as health status and reported levels of stress. Our analysis presents results separately for men and women, owing to established gender differences in these health behaviours (see Cooper, Ginn and Arber, 1999).

Unlike the measures of social support used in Chapter 6, the HSE data include a more 'subjective' measure of social support based on personal feelings about family and friends rather than frequency of contact with these groups (Appendix B). A series of seven questions ask whether the individual feels loved, happy, important and accepted, and can rely on others for care, support and encouragement. Together, this information provides a measure of perceived social support. These responses are scored according to whether the respondent considers that they are true, partly true or untrue and respondents are classified into one of the following groups: no lack of social support, some lack of social support and severe lack of social support (see Appendix B for further details). Since this measure differs from the measures of social support based on types of social contact (discussed in Chapter 5), the following section analyses variation according to key socioeconomic and demographic characteristics of men and women before considering any association with their health behaviour.

Perceived social support

Figure 7.1 shows the percentage of men and women in different age groups who are classed as having a severe lack of social support. Women are less likely to have a severe lack of social support than men in each age group. For both sexes, the oldest and youngest age groups are least likely to have adequate social support from friends and family. This is especially marked among men, with 20% of 16–24-year-olds and 21% aged 85 and above having a severe lack of social support compared with 15% of men aged 45–54 years.

Living arrangements are significantly associated with levels of social support (Figure 7.2). Those who are divorced/separated or single are more likely to have a severe lack of social support than the married, but within these groups living alone is more strongly associated with the absence of social support than living with others. Approximately 30% of male divorcees who live alone have a severe lack of social support from friends and family which falls to 22% among the divorced/separated living with other people; only 14% of married men have a severe lack of social support. Men who are widowed and living alone are more likely to have a severe lack of social support than widowers living with others, but there is no difference between the married and widowers living with others. Women who are single and living alone are most likely to have a severe lack of social support, but

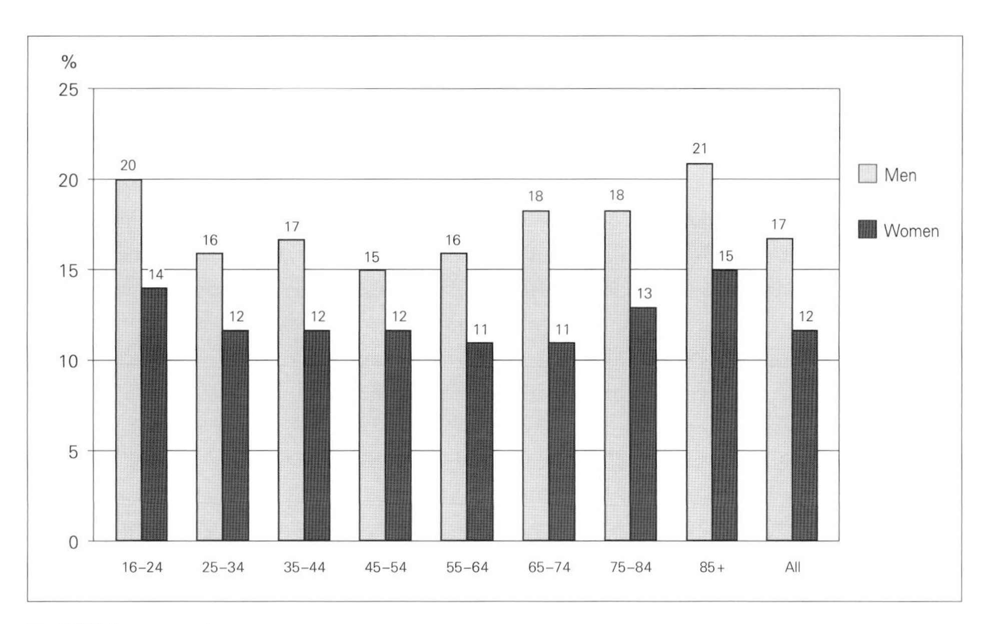

P < 0.001 for men and women
Source: Health Survey for England, 1993 and 1994

***Fig. 7.1.* Percentage of men and women with a severe lack of social support by age group**

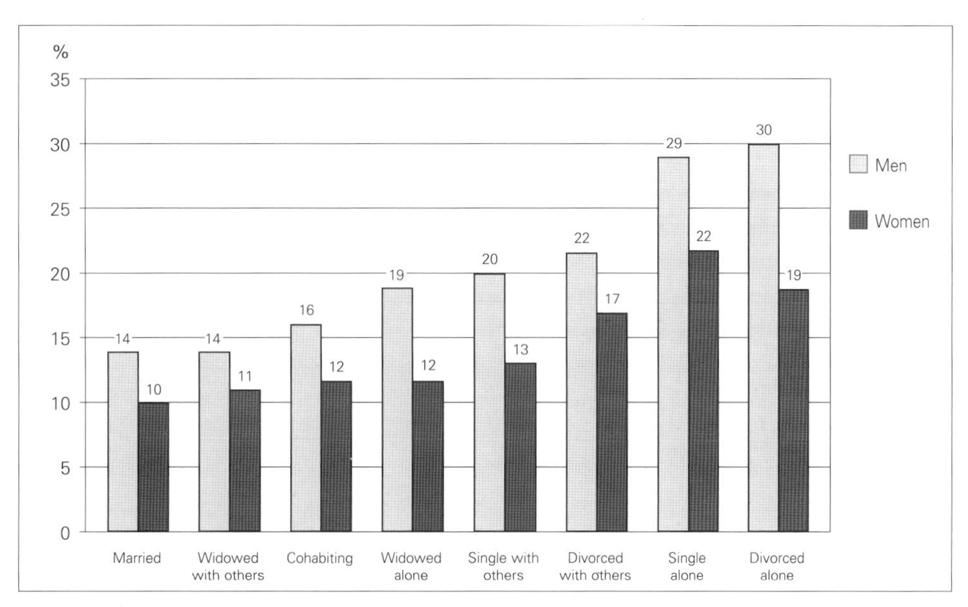

P < 0.001 for men and women
Source: Health Survey for England, 1993 and 1994

***Fig. 7.2.* Percentage of men and women with a severe lack of social support by living arrangements: men and women aged 16 +**

the proportion is nearly halved for single women living with others. Unlike the never married or divorced, being widowed is not strongly associated with a severe lack of social support, with little variation among women who are widows, married or cohabiting.

These results are consistent with those found in Chapter 5 using frequency of contact with friends and relatives as an indicator of social support. Men are more likely than women to have infrequent contact with friends and relatives (Table 5.1) and a severe lack of perceived social support. The divorced/separated are less likely to report close contact with friends and relatives (Figure 5.5) and more likely to have a severe lack of perceived social support than the married, with additional differences in social support according to whether or not the individual lives alone or with other people.

Figure 7.3 shows that paid employment is positively associated with perceived social support. More than one-quarter of men who are unemployed or economically inactive have a severe lack of social support compared with under 15% of full-time workers. These differences are much less marked for women, but the unemployed and other inactive group are more likely to have a severe lack of social support than women who are in paid employment, are full-time students or retired.

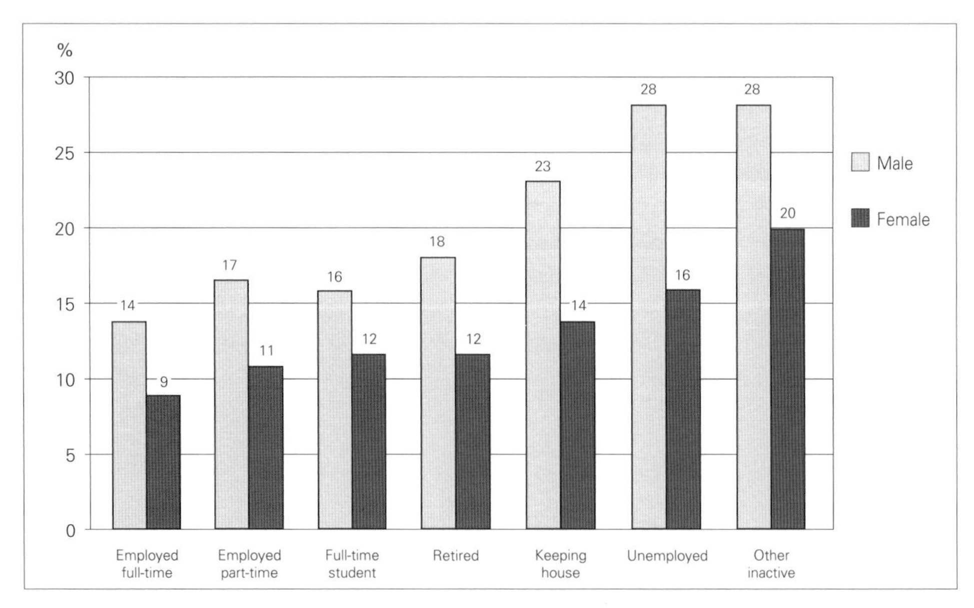

$P < 0.001$ for men and women

Source: Health Survey for England, 1993 and 1994

***Fig. 7.3.* Percentage of men and women with a severe lack of social support by employment status**

We begin our analysis by investigating how this indicator of perceived social support influences the likelihood of having a healthy diet for men and women in different age groups and socioeconomic circumstances. Smoking behaviour is then related to measures of social support and social capital, using data from the HSE and HALS respectively.

Quality of diet

The Health Survey for England asks respondents to report their consumption of a range of different foods, and we used this information to assign a 'diet score' indicating the relative 'healthiness', or quality, of their diet. A large negative score indicates an unhealthy diet high in sugar, cakes, salt and saturated fats and low in fruit, vegetables and fibre-rich foods, whilst a high positive score reflects the reverse pattern (see Appendix B). The overall mean diet score is approximately zero, but women's diets are more healthy than men's, with average scores of 1.21 and –0.86 respectively.

Figure 7.4 presents the average diet scores of men and women in different age groups. There is a curvilinear relationship between age and quality of diet for both sexes, with the poorest diet among those aged 16–24 and 85+ and the healthiest diet among those in their late 40s and early 50s. Women aged 16–24 have the worst average diet score of –4.6, which increases to +2.6 for those aged 45–54 and falls below zero for women aged 75 and above. With the exception of the youngest age group, men have lower average diet scores than women in each age group; men's score only rises above zero between age 45 and 64.

The quality of diet eaten varies linearly with the Personal Deprivation Index score (Figure 7.5). Men in the most materially deprived group (score 4+) have the poorest diet, with an average diet score of –3.9. This compares with a diet score of –2.3 for those with a PDI score of 2 and a diet score of approximately zero for the most materially advantaged group. A similar gradient in diet scores is found for women, with corresponding PDI scores of –2.7, –0.3 and 2.5. Men and women in materially disadvantaged groups are much less likely to eat fresh fruit, vegetables and high-fibre foods than those with adequate material resources. This suggests that low income and lack of access to a car can place constraints on the type of foods they can obtain.

Occupational social class is strongly associated with quality of diet based on the consumption of vegetables, sugar and fat (see Appendix B). Figure 7.6 shows a linear class gradient for both sexes in each age group below 75 years. Men and women in the professional and managerial classes are substantially more likely to have a healthy diet than those in the manual classes. Women who have never worked are more likely to eat healthily than those in the unskilled class, but less likely than women employed in non-manual occupations.

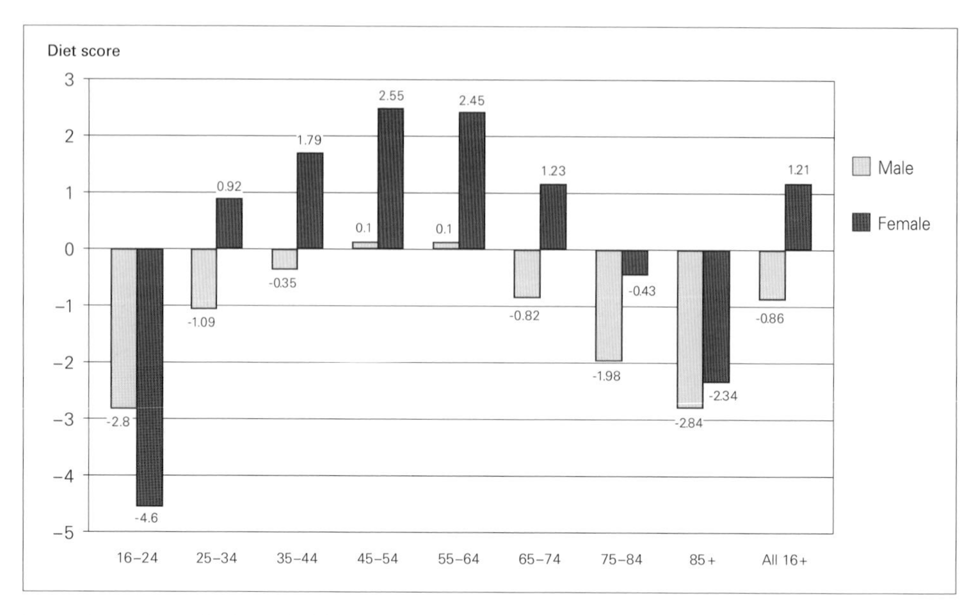

Source: Health Survey for England, 1993 and 1994

***Fig. 7.4.* Mean diet scores for men and women aged 16+ by age group**

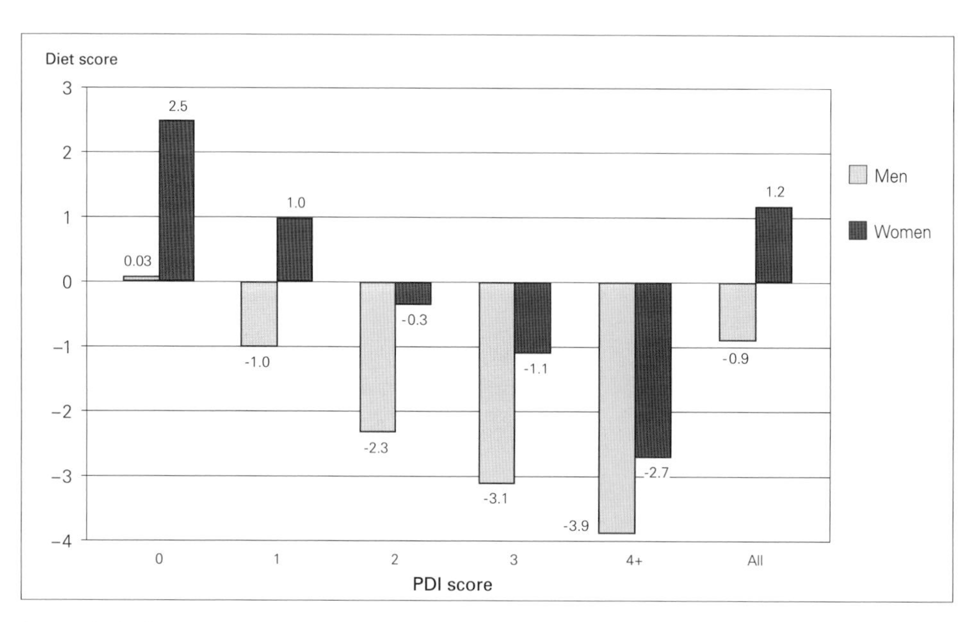

Source: Health Survey for England, 1993 and 1994

***Fig. 7.5.* Mean diet scores for men and women aged 16+ by Personal Deprivation Index**

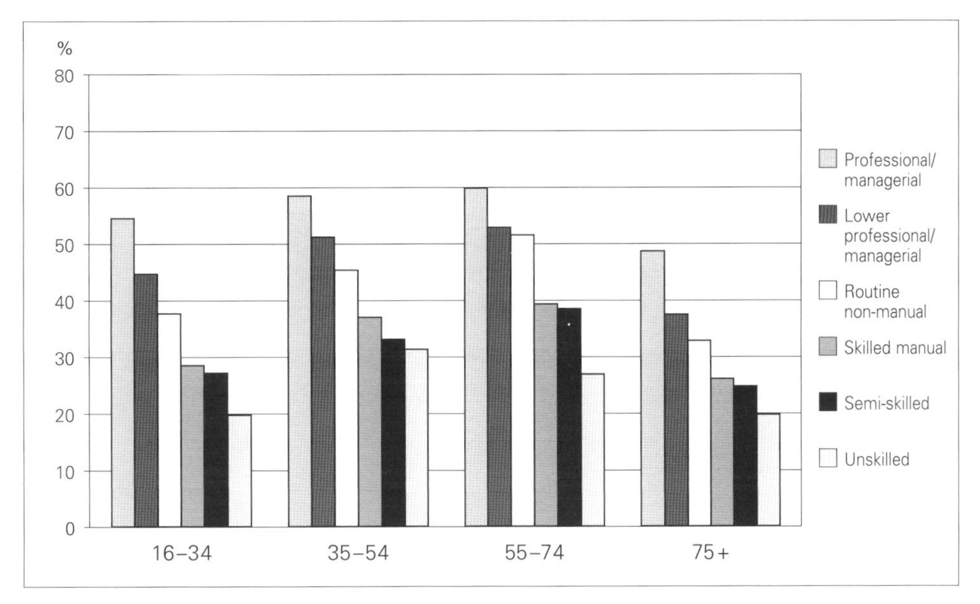

Men

$P < 0.001$ for all age groups

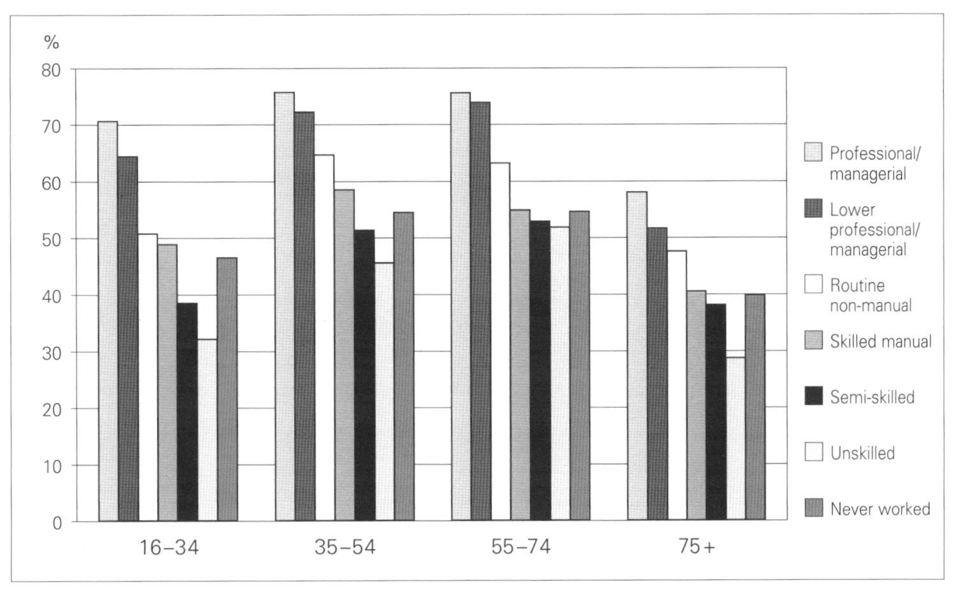

Women

$P < 0.001$ for all age groups

Source: Health Survey for England, 1993 and 1994

***Fig. 7.6.* Percentage of men and women with a healthy diet* by age and socioeconomic group†**

*Defined as a positive diet score (see Appendix B); †Actual percentages are listed in Appendix E.

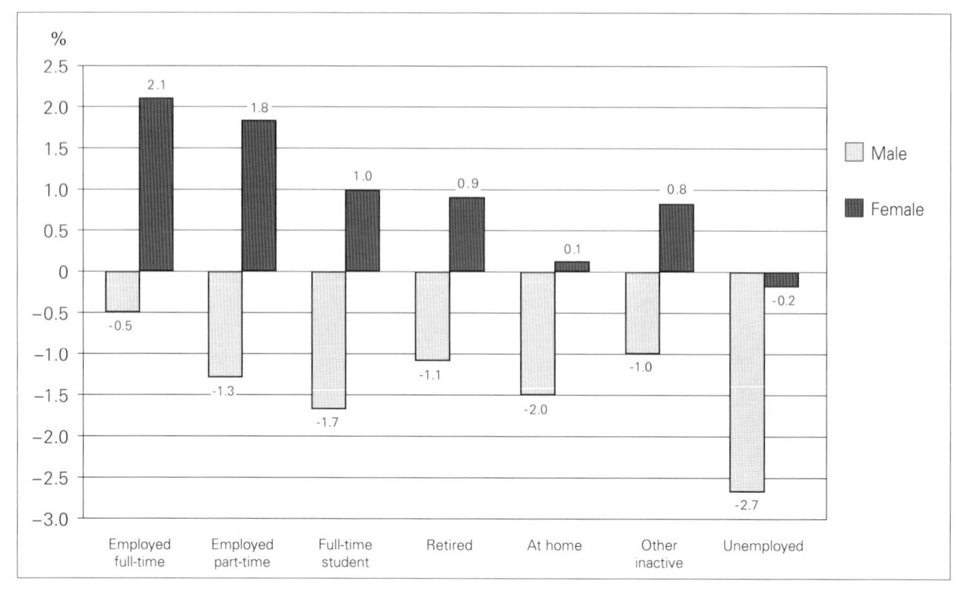

Source: Health Survey for England, 1993 and 1994

***Fig. 7.7.* Mean diet scores for men and women aged 16+ by employment status**

Being in paid employment is associated with a healthier diet (Figure 7.7). The average diet score of the unemployed is –2.7 for men and –0.2 for women compared with –0.5 and +2.1 respectively for men and women employed full time. The gender difference in quality of diet is particularly marked among those who are employed part-time.

Figure 7.8 shows the average diet scores of men and women according to perceived social support from friends and relatives. For men, a severe lack of social support is strongly associated with a poor diet, as shown by the large negative score of –3.5 for men aged 16–34 compared with a score of –1 for men of the same age with no lack of social support. For women in each age group, the average diet score is highest for those with adequate social support and lowest among those with a severe lack of social support. The effect of lack of social support in diet is much stronger among younger than older age groups.

The results confirm previous research (Cooper, Ginn and Arber, 1999; Ginn, Arber and Cooper, 1998), showing a strong relationship between older people's health behaviour and structural factors, with the lower social classes and the most materially deprived least likely to engage in health-promoting activity. A poor diet was significantly more likely among those with a severe lack of perceived social support than for those with sufficient social support from family and friends.

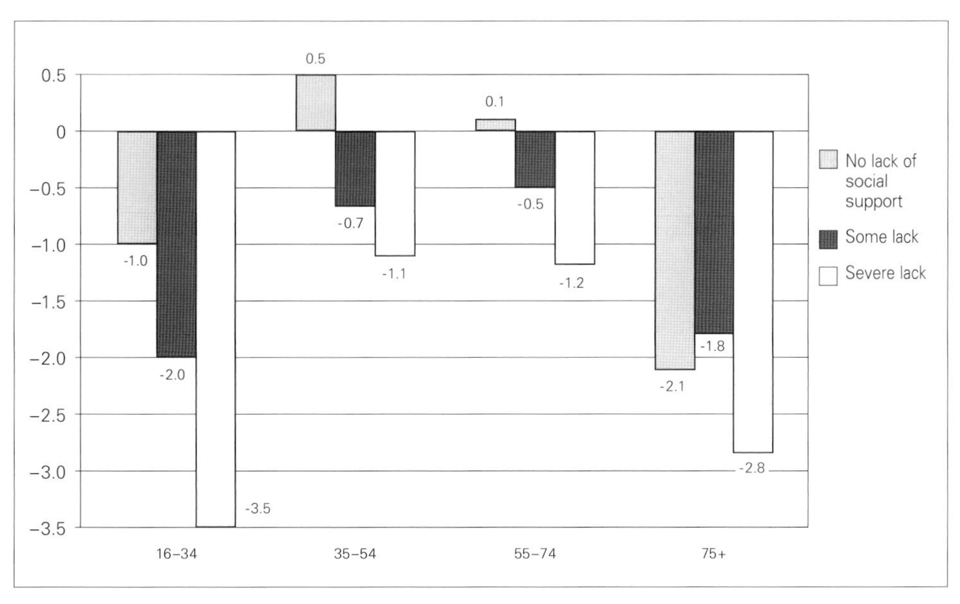

Men

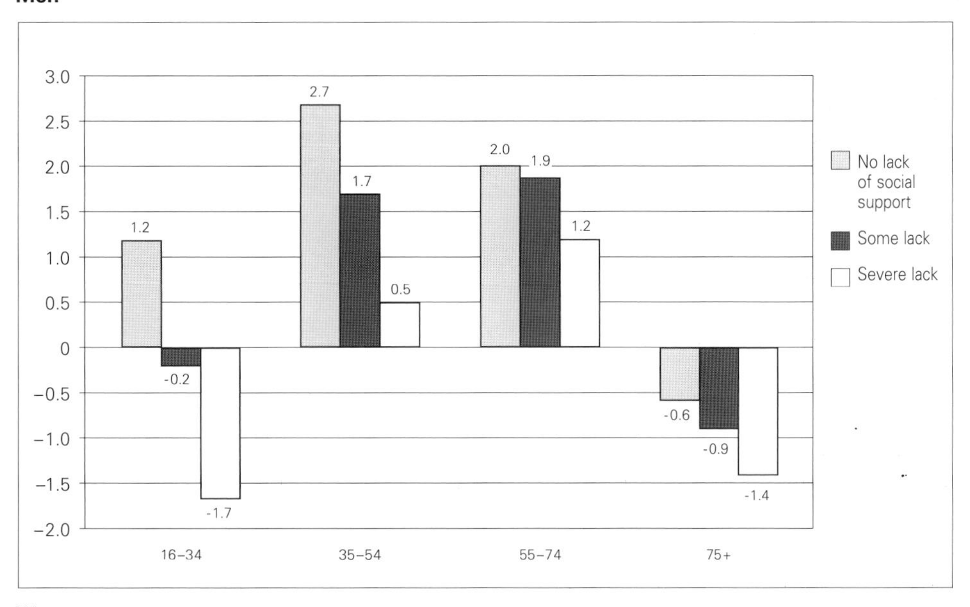

Women

Source: Health Survey for England, 1993 and 1994

***Fig. 7.8.* Mean diet scores for men and women by age group and level of perceived social support**

Multivariate analysis: quality of diet

Logistic regression analysis is used to assess the relative influence of socioeconomic position and social support on diet quality. Using the HSE data, models are first presented which show the odds of having a diet score less than zero, according to differences in socioeconomic position, age and health status. Social factors are then added to the models to examine how they are independently related to diet after controlling for the other variables in the model. Finally, a measure of stress (see Appendix B) is added in a third set of models to assess whether a high level of stress is independently associated with this health behaviour.

Table 7.1 presents the odds ratios of having a poor diet separately for men and women aged 16 and above. Model 1 shows that men aged 16–24 years and women aged 85+ are most likely to have a poorer than average diet after controlling for health status, socioeconomic group and material resources. For both sexes, a good diet is positively associated with good general health. However, those with a chronic illness are more likely to have a healthy diet than those without. This is likely to reflect the negative effects of a poor diet on health together with a tendency for those with chronic health problems, such as diabetes, to improve their diet.

Class is strongly associated with diet; the odds of a poorer than average diet are over two times higher for men and women in manual occupations compared with the professional/managerial group, and a poor diet is also more likely among those who have never worked relative to this group. In addition to social class, material deprivation is strongly associated with a poorer diet. The odds of a poorer than average diet are significantly increased by 2.47 for men and 2.80 for women with a PDI score of 4 or more compared to those with a PDI score of zero.

Both living arrangements and social support are significantly associated with diet after controlling for these structural factors (Model 2). There is no difference in quality of diet between those who are married and cohabiting. Women who are widowed and living with others have a poorer diet than married women, whilst lone widows have a better diet than married women. The results suggest a similar trend for men, although falling short of statistical significance. Single men living alone are least likely to have a poor quality diet, whilst the diet of single women and the divorced/separated does not differ significantly from the married after controlling for differences in socioeconomic position and social support.

Diet is strongly associated with social support; a severe lack of social support significantly increases the odds of a poorer than average diet by 44% for men and 35% for women compared to those having no lack of social support. (A poor diet is also more likely among

Table 7.1. Odds ratios of having a poorer than average diet: men and women aged 16+

	Men			Women		
	Model 1	Model 2	Model 3	Model 1	Model 2	Model 3
Age	†††	†††	†††	†††	†††	†††
16–24	1.00	1.00	1.00	1.00	1.00	1.00
25–34	0.59***	0.63***	0.63***	0.82**	0.80**	0.80**
35–44	0.56***	0.58***	0.58***	0.65***	0.63***	0.62***
45–54	0.48***	0.50***	0.49***	0.56***	0.54***	0.53***
55–64	0.43***	0.45***	0.43***	0.52***	0.51***	0.49***
65–74	0.52***	0.55***	0.51***	0.60***	0.60***	0.58***
75–84	0.79*	0.84	0.78	0.87	0.90	0.86
85+	0.89	0.92	0.84	1.54**	1.61**	1.52**
General health	††	†	†	†††	††	†††
Good	1.00	1.00	1.00	1.00	1.00	1.00
Fair	1.17**	1.14**	1.15**	1.29***	1.25***	1.27***
Bad	1.18	1.15	1.18	1.20*	1.15	1.18
Chronic illness	†††	†††	†††	†††	†††	†††
No long-standing illness	1.00	1.00	1.00	1.00	1.00	1.00
Chronic illness	0.81***	0.81***	0.84***	0.82***	0.82***	0.83***
Socioeconomic group	†††	†††	†††	†††	†††	†††
Professional/managerial	1.00	1.00	1.00	1.00	1.00	1.00
Lower professional and managerial	1.29***	1.29***	1.30***	1.23*	1.21*	1.20*
Junior non-manual	1.49***	1.46***	1.45***	1.83***	1.78***	1.74***
Skilled manual	2.14***	2.08***	2.04***	2.02***	1.95***	1.90***
Semi-skilled	2.14***	2.05***	2.00***	2.48***	2.37***	2.30***
Unskilled	2.60***	2.52***	2.43***	2.72***	2.59***	2.51***
Never worked	1.43***	1.36**	1.35**	1.92***	1.85***	1.81***
PDI score	†††	†††	†††	†††	†††	†††
0	1.00	1.00	1.00	1.00	1.00	1.00
1	1.18***	1.19***	1.18***	1.33***	1.34***	1.34***
2	1.57***	1.60***	1.58***	1.70***	1.74***	1.74***
3	1.91***	1.98***	1.95***	2.10***	2.15***	2.15***
4+	2.47***	2.55***	2.51***	2.80***	2.85***	2.83***
Living arrangements		†††	†††		†	†
Married		1.00	1.00		1.00	1.00
Cohabiting		0.96	0.96		0.92	0.92
Single with others		1.04	1.03		0.94	0.93
Widowed with others		1.44	1.45		1.25*	1.25*
Divorced/separated with others		1.20	1.19		0.98	0.99
Single lives alone		0.69***	0.69***		0.87	0.87
Widowed lives alone		0.88	0.87		0.84*	0.84*
Divorced/separated lives alone		0.84	0.83		0.93	0.93

Continued on next page

Table 7.1. *continued*

	Men			Women		
	Model 1	**Model 2**	**Model 3**	**Model 1**	**Model 2**	**Model 3**
Social support		†††	†††		†††	†††
No lack of social support		1.00	1.00		1.00	1.00
Some lack of social support		1.16***	1.17***		1.16***	1.17***
Severe lack of social support		1.44***	1.44***		1.35***	1.37***
Stress			††			††
None			1.00			1.00
Little			0.83***			0.92
Moderate amount			0.88*			0.84**
Quite a lot			0.83**			0.80***
Great deal			0.84			1.01
N =	14 046			16 586		
ΔLR (Δdf)	972.4 (20)	79.3 (9)	17.4 (4)	1297.2 (20)	55.5 (9)	18.5 (4)

Significance of difference from reference category: $*P < 0.05$; $**P < 0.01$; $***P < 0.001$
Significance of variable in the model: †$P < 0.05$; ††$P < 0.01$; †††$P < 0.001$
Source: Health Survey for England, 1993 and 1994

men and women experiencing some lack of social support relative to this group.) The strong effect of structural factors on diet is little affected by including social support in the models.

There is no evidence that the quality of diet deteriorates as levels of reported stress increase (Model 3). The results show the opposite trend, with a poor diet less likely among men and women experiencing stress. The effect of social support on diet remains unaltered when stress is added to the model, which suggests that the influence of social support on diet is not mediated by stress.

Cigarette smoking

This section uses data from the HSE to consider differences in smoking for men and women aged 16 and above according to perceived social support. The analysis is supplemented where appropriate with results from the HEA Health and Lifestyle Survey (HALS) showing variation in smoking behaviour of adults aged 16–74 years using the measures of social capital and community participation introduced in Chapter 5. Equivalent measures of smoking are used in both surveys (see Appendices A and B), but it is important to be aware of the different sample design of the HSE and HALS (see Chapter 5).

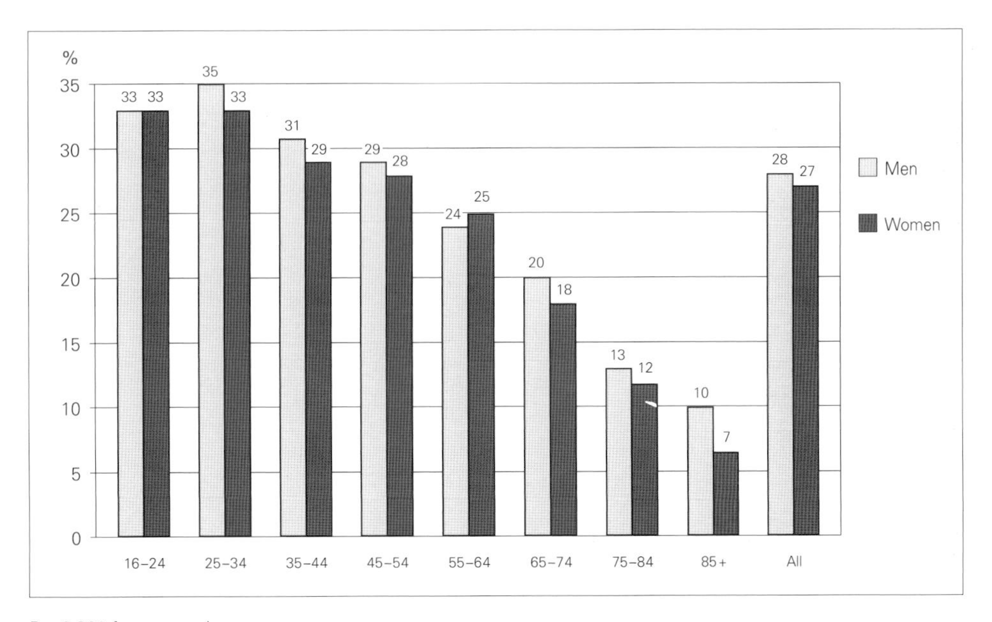

P < 0.001 for men and women
Source: Health Survey for England, 1993 and 1994

***Fig. 7.9.* Percentage of men and women currently smoking cigarettes by age group**

The HSE data show the well known age-related decrease in smoking for both sexes (Figure 7.9). There is no gender difference in smoking for 16–24-year-olds, but men above this age are slightly more likely to smoke than women, with the greatest gender difference in smoking among the oldest group, aged 85 and above.

Smoking is strongly associated with material living conditions for men and women of all ages (Figure 7.10). For adults under 75 years with a maximum Personal Deprivation Score of 4+, the proportion of current smokers is more than doubled compared to those with no material disadvantage (PDI score 0). This gradient in smoking is also evident among older age groups: 27% of the most materially disadvantaged men and 20% of women aged 75+ in this group are smokers compared to 5% and 8% of older men and women who do not live in materially deprived conditions.

Figure 7.11 confirms that social support from friends and relatives is associated with lower levels of smoking among men and women, suggesting that lack of perceived support from these sources may induce health-damaging behaviour. For those under 75 years there is a clear gradient in smoking according to the adequacy of social support. Over 40% of 16–34-year-olds who have a severe lack of social support are current smokers, whereas less than a third of men and women smoke among those with social support. Differences in smoking according to level of social support are less pronounced for men aged over 75 and women over 55 years.

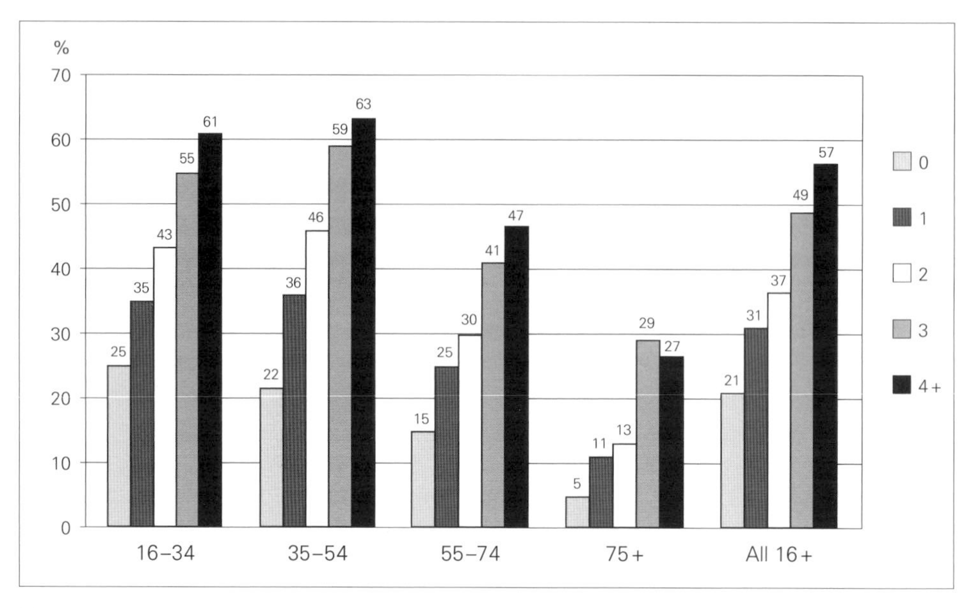

Men

$P < 0.001$ for all age groups

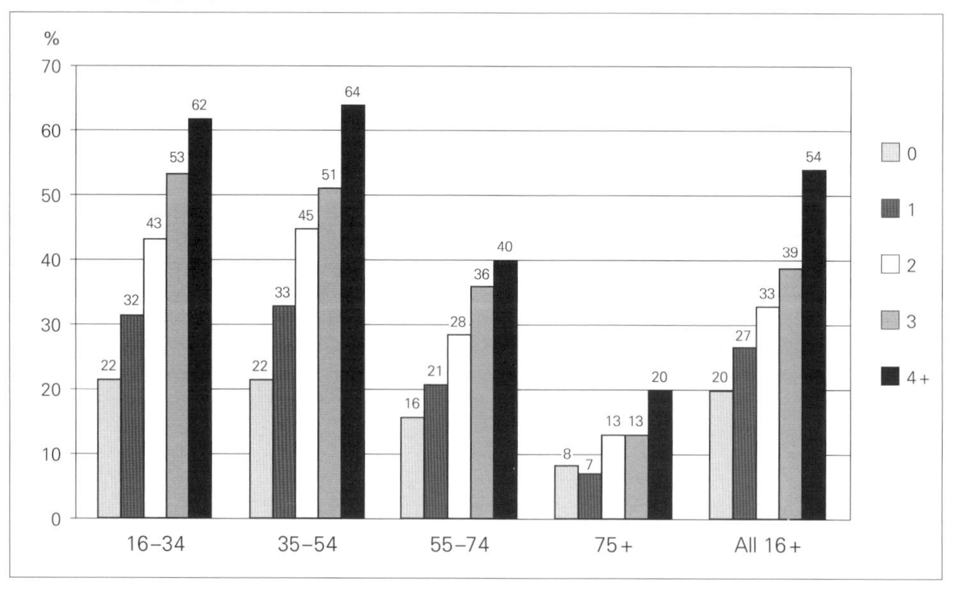

Women

$P < 0.001$ for all age groups

Source: Health Survey for England, 1993 and 1994

Fig. 7.10.* Percentage of men and women currently smoking by age group and Personal Deprivation Score

*The PDI score increases as the level of material deprivation becomes greater (see Appendix B).

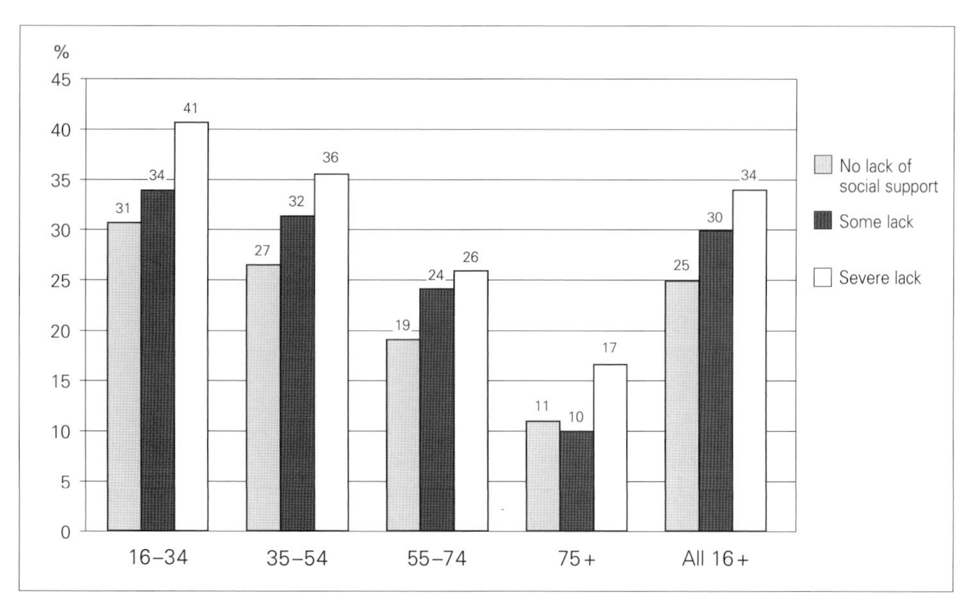

Men

$P < 0.001$ for 16–34, 35–54, 55–74. P (ns) for 75+

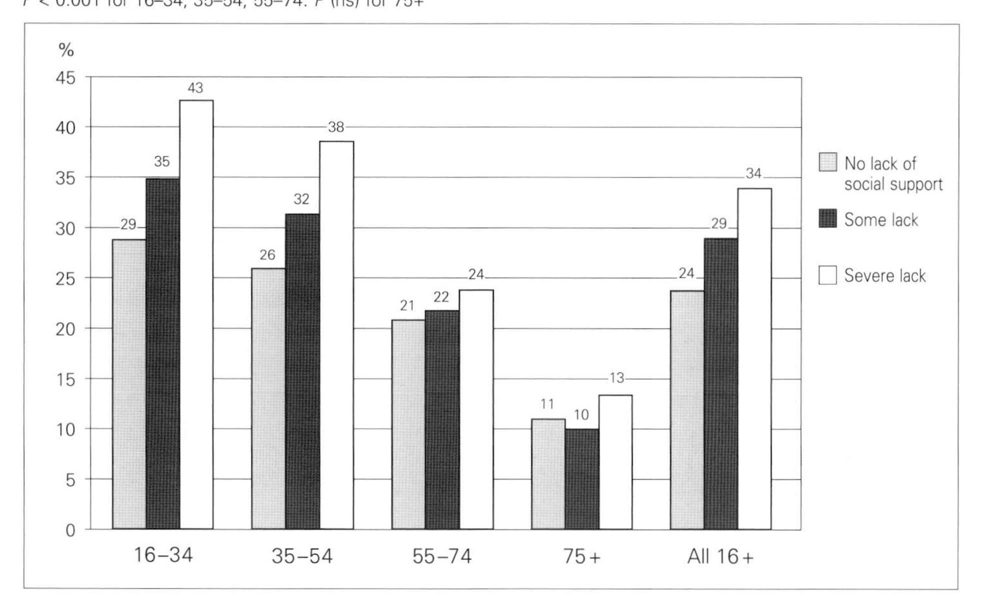

Women

$P < 0.001$ for 16–34, 35–54. P (ns) for 55–74 and 75+

Source: Health Survey for England, 1993 and 1994

***Fig. 7.11.* Percentage of men and women currently smoking by age group and social support**

In HALS, regular smokers who have tried to give up are asked to give their reasons for re-starting. Of those who were unsuccessful in quitting smoking, 8% said they re-started because of stress and this was significantly more likely among women than men. However, men were more likely than women to say they re-started because of encouragement to smoke from friends and colleagues, in other words – peer group pressure. Approximately 5% of those who had re-started said that help and support from family members would aid them in giving up smoking, while 3% indicated that support from friends would be beneficial.

Figure 7.12 uses HALS data to examine the relationship between our measure of neighbourhood social capital based on perception of the locality (see Chapter 6 and Appendix A) and smoking in those aged 16–74 years. For women, smoking is associated with low neighbourhood social capital. Only 20% of women living in areas with very high social capital are smokers, but over 30% smoke among those with a medium level of social capital and 40% when neighbourhood social capital is low. This consistent gradient in smoking rates according to the level of social capital is found for all age groups of women, with smoking approximately doubled for those reporting low social capital relative to those with very high levels of social capital. In contrast, the association between social capital and smoking is less consistent for men. Men with a low level of social capital are most likely to be smokers in each age group, but the proportion of smokers does not consistently reduce as the level of neighbourhood social capital increases.

Table 7.2. Percentage of men and women currently smoking by community activity and age group

	Men			Women		
	Community activity	**No community activity**	***P* (Sig)**	**Community activity**	**No community activity**	***P* (Sig)**
16–34	19	38	< 0.001	24	35	< 0.01
N =	(145)	(866)		(181)	(798)	
35–54	24	37	< 0.01	16	39	< 0.001
N =	(169)	(690)		(230)	(632)	
55–74	18	29	< 0.05	12	26	< 0.001
N =	(124)	(483)		(221)	(449)	
All 16–74	21	35	< 0.001	17	34	< 0.001
N =	(438)	(2 039)		(632)	(1 878)	

Source: HEA Health and Lifestyles Survey, 1992

Individuals' involvement in community activities, such as voluntary or religious groups, is strongly associated with their smoking behaviour. Table 7.2 shows that the smoking rate is 21% among men who engage in community activity but 35% among those who do not. These differences in smoking are even more marked for women, increasing for those aged 35–54 years from 16% among those who are active in the community to 39% among the non-active. Thus, neighbourhood social capital, community activity and social support are all associated with a lower likelihood of smoking, particularly among women.

Men

16–34 $P < 0.01$; 35–54; 55–74 P (ns); 16–74 $P < 0.01$

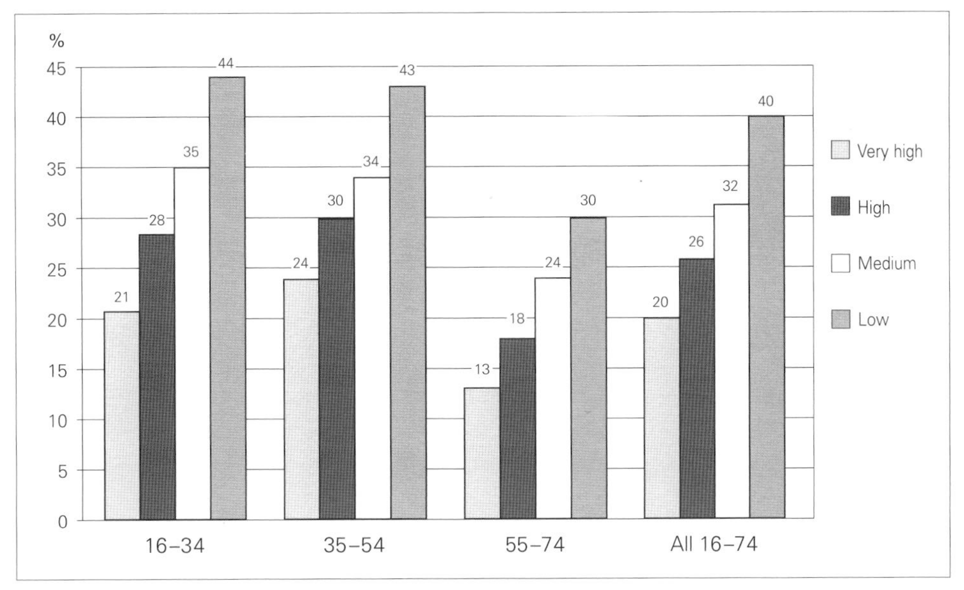

Women

16–34; 35–54 $P < 0.001$; 55–74 $P < 0.01$; 16–74 $P < 0.001$

Source: HEA Health and Lifestyles Survey, 1992

***Fig. 7.12.* Percentage of men and women currently smoking by neighbourhood social capital and age group**

Multivariate analysis: cigarette smoking

Data from the HEA Health and Lifestyles Survey were used to assess the relationship between smoking and social capital. Indicators of socioeconomic position and social capital were entered into a logistic regression model which also controlled for age and differences in health status and reported stress. Graphs of the odds ratios from this model are presented separately for measures of social capital and socioeconomic position to show the relative association of these factors with smoking.

Table 7.3, Model 1 presents the odds of being a current smoker for adults in the Health Survey for England, after controlling for age, health status, socioeconomic position and material resources. For both sexes, the likelihood of being a smoker significantly decreases with advancing age after adjusting for the other factors in the model. The odds ratio of smoking is reduced by 88% for men and 91% for women aged 85+ compared to the youngest age group of 16–24-year-olds.

Men and women who report good general health are least likely to smoke, with the odds ratio of smoking significantly increased by 60% for men and 55% for women who rate their health as 'bad'. In contrast, the likelihood of being a current smoker is reduced for those reporting chronic illness compared to those with no long-standing illness – a difference which is statistically significant after adjusting for age, socioeconomic position and subjective health status. These results are likely to reflect the adverse effects of smoking on health and life expectancy as well as an increased tendency to quit smoking because of long-term ill health.

Smoking is strongly associated with structural factors. The odds of being a smoker are greatest for those in the unskilled group relative to the professional/managerial class (the reference category), whilst women who have never worked are significantly less likely to smoke than the reference category. The likelihood of smoking substantially increases as material living conditions worsen. Among those with a Personal Deprivation Index score of 4+, the odds of smoking are 3.8 times higher for men and 4.74 times higher for women compared to those who are materially advantaged (PDI score 0). After controlling for socioeconomic group and material resources, employment status is not a significant predictor of smoking.

Lack of social support and certain living arrangements were both significantly associated with smoking after controlling for structural factors. Including these variables improved the fit of the model by 77.9 for men and 87.6 for women (Model 2). There is a significant difference in likelihood of smoking between the married and the cohabiting, with men and women in the latter group being more likely to smoke. Men who are widowed and

Table 7.3. Odds of smoking cigarettes: men and women aged 16+

	Men			Women		
	Model 1	Model 2	Model 3	Model 1	Model 2	Model 3
Age	†††	†††	†††	†††	†††	†††
16–24	1.00	1.00	1.00	1.00	1.00	1.00
25–34	1.02	0.95	0.95	0.97	0.99	0.99
35–44	0.95	0.88	0.88	0.89	0.93	0.92
45–54	0.81**	0.76**	0.75**	0.86	0.92	0.91
55–64	0.55***	0.51***	0.50***	0.64***	0.71***	0.70***
65–74	0.40***	0.37***	0.36***	0.34***	0.38***	0.38***
75–84	0.19***	0.17***	0.17***	0.16***	0.18***	0.18***
85+	0.12***	0.10***	0.10***	0.09***	0.10***	0.10***
General health	†††	†††	†††	†††	†††	†††
Good	1.00	1.00	1.00	1.00	1.00	1.00
Fair	1.58***	1.58***	1.58***	1.43***	1.42***	1.40***
Bad	1.60***	1.59***	1.59***	1.55***	1.52***	1.43***
Chronic illness	†††	†††	†††	†††	†††	†††
No long-standing illness	1.00	1.00	1.00	1.00	1.00	1.00
Chronic illness	0.86***	0.85***	0.86***	0.86***	0.85***	0.85***
Socioeconomic group	†††	†††	†††	†††	†††	†††
Professional/managerial	1.00	1.00	1.00	1.00	1.00	1.00
Lower professional and managerial	1.40***	1.39***	1.40***	0.95	0.98	0.99
Junior non-manual	1.38***	1.37***	1.38***	1.05	1.10	1.13
Skilled manual	1.89***	1.86***	1.86**	1.38**	1.44***	1.48***
Semi-skilled	1.90***	1.87***	1.87***	1.34**	1.40***	1.45***
Unskilled	2.28***	2.29***	2.27***	1.47***	1.58***	1.63***
Never worked	0.87	0.91	0.91	0.61***	0.66***	0.67***
PDI score	†††	†††	†††	†††	†††	†††
0	1.00	1.00	1.00	1.00	1.00	1.00
1	1.65***	1.62***	1.61***	1.60***	1.52***	1.52***
2	2.17***	2.10***	2.09***	2.50***	2.27***	2.29***
3	3.54***	3.33***	3.31***	3.37***	2.90***	2.91***
4+	3.80***	3.47***	3.44***	4.74***	3.91***	3.93***
Living arrangements		†††	†††		†††	†††
Married		1.00	1.00		1.00	1.00
Cohabiting		1.52***	1.53***		1.63***	1.62***
Single with others		0.91	0.91		1.09	1.08
Widowed with others		1.37	1.39		1.29*	1.29
Divorced/separated with others		1.65***	1.65***		1.56***	1.52***
Single lives alone		0.95	0.96		1.34***	1.32***
Widowed lives alone		1.39*	1.39*		1.06	1.05
Divorced/separated lives alone		1.61***	1.60***		1.48***	1.45***
Social support		†	†		††	††
No lack of social support		1.00	1.00		1.00	1.00
Some lack of social support		1.10*	1.11*		1.11*	1.11*
Severe lack of support		1.10	1.11		1.19**	1.17**

Continued on next page

Table 7.3. *continued*

	Men			Women		
	Model 1	Model 2	Model 3	Model 1	Model 2	Model 3
Stress			ns			†††
None			1.00			1.00
Little			0.90			0.92
Moderate amount			0.92			0.92
Quite a lot			0.92			1.09
Great deal			1.10			1.42***
N =	14 171			16 797		
ΔLLR (Δdf)	1381.5 (20)	77.9 (9)	6.9 (4)	1585.9 (20)	87.6 (9)	32.0 (4)

Significance of difference from reference category: **P* < 0.05; ***P* < 0.01; ****P* < 0.001
Significance of variable in the model: †*P* < 0.05; ††*P* < 0.01; †††*P* < 0.001
Source: Health Survey for England, 1993 and 1994

living alone are significantly more likely to be current smokers than the married, but there is no such difference for women. Being divorced/separated is strongly associated with smoking regardless of whether the individual lives alone or with others. The odds ratios of smoking are significantly increased by over 60% for divorced/separated men relative to married men. The odds for divorced/separated women are increased by approximately half compared with married women. Whereas single men are no more likely to smoke than married, single women living alone are more likely to smoke than married women.

Smoking is least likely among men and women who have social support. The odds ratio of current smoking is significantly higher for those who have some lack of social support and for women with a severe lack of social support. The positive relationship between lack of social support and smoking remains after controlling for structural factors and living arrangements, showing that perceived social support from friends and relatives has an independent influence on this health behaviour. However, adding this variable to the model has little effect on the much stronger relationship between structural factors and smoking.

Model 3 shows an association between stress and current smoking among women, but not men. Women with high reported stress levels have odds of smoking 42% higher than those with the lowest stress. This may be a response to feelings of stress (Graham, 1993). There is no evidence that stress can account for the greater smoking of men and women who lack social support, as this relationship remains unchanged when stress is included in the model.

Using data from HALS, we next analyse how smoking is related to social capital and community activity. Figure 7.13 presents the odds ratios of smoking after adjusting for socioeconomic and socio-demographic factors, namely age, sex, social class, employment

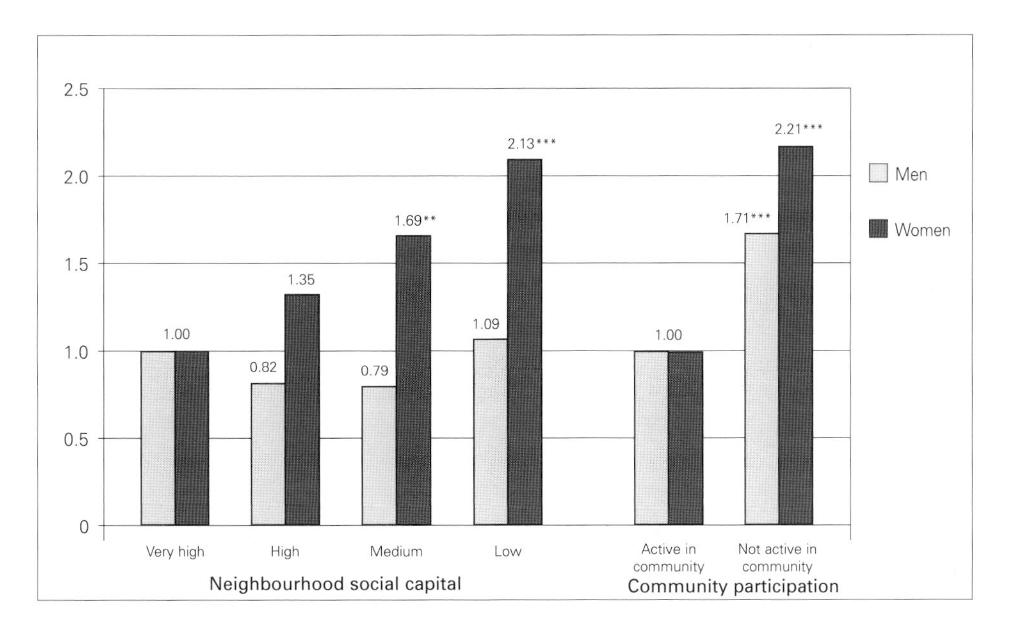

Significance of difference from reference category (value = 1.00): $*P < 0.05$; $**P < 0.01$; $***P < 0.001$
Source: HEA Health and Lifestyles Survey, 1992

***Fig. 7.13.* Odds ratios of current smoking by measures of social capital: for men and women aged 16–74 years after controlling for age, socioeconomic position, health status and reported stress**

status and material deprivation (see Appendix B). For women, the likelihood of smoking consistently increases as the level of neighbourhood social capital decreases, but this gradient is not evident for men after controlling for the other variables in the model. For women, the odds of smoking are 2.13 times higher when neighbourhood social capital is low, compared with the reference category (very high neighbourhood social capital). For both sexes, those involved in community activity are less likely to smoke. The odds ratio of current smoking is significantly increased to 1.71 for men and to 2.21 for women who do not participate in any voluntary or community group activity.

The benefits of neighbourhood social capital and community participation on smoking behaviour exist independently of age, socioeconomic group, material deprivation, health status and reported levels of stress. However, Figure 7.14 shows that structural factors (social class and material deprivation) are more strongly associated with smoking than neighbourhood social capital and community activity.

For men there is a statistically significant association between smoking and social class, with the odds of smoking 3.26 times higher for men in social classes IV and V compared

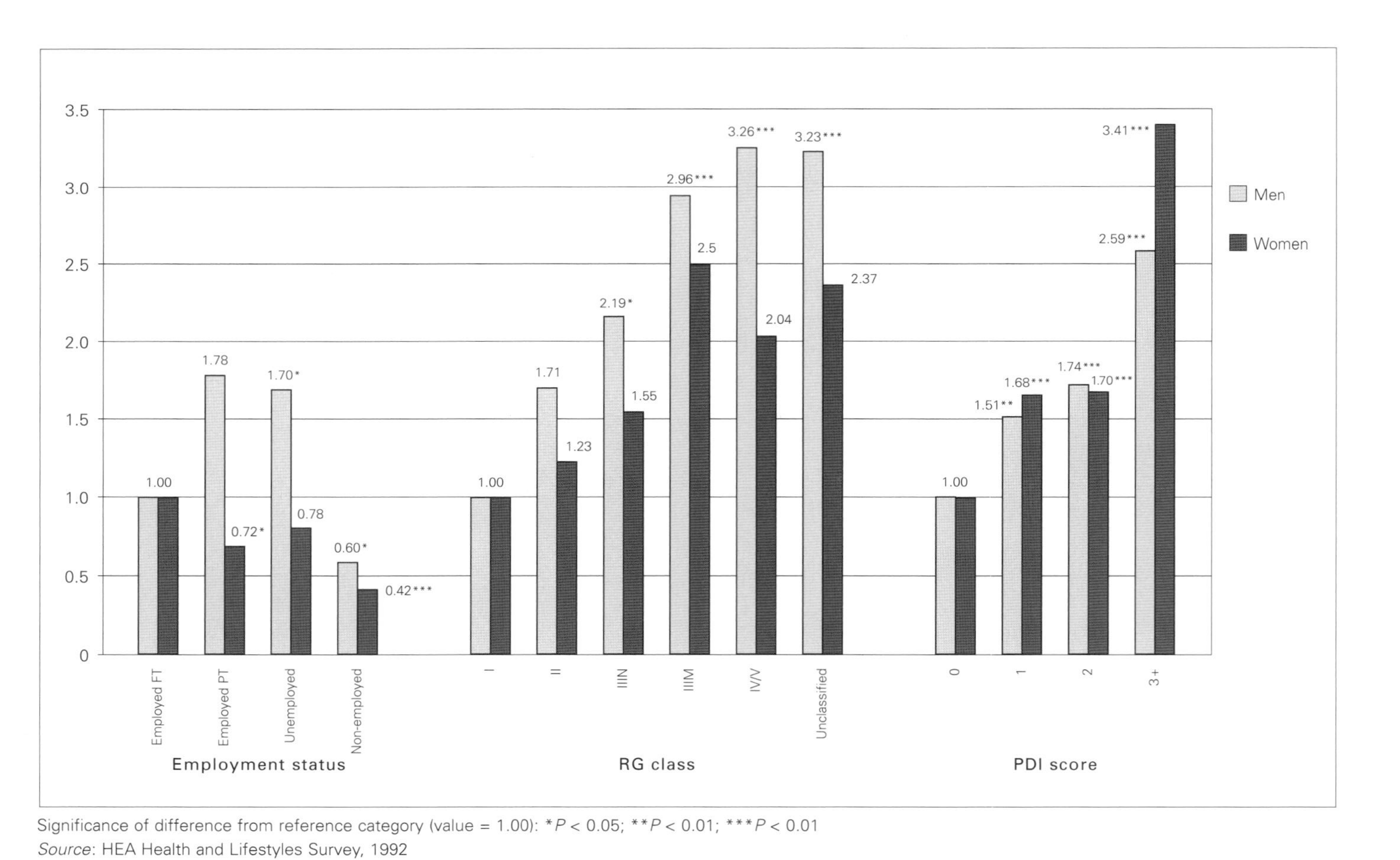

Significance of difference from reference category (value = 1.00): $*P < 0.05$; $**P < 0.01$; $***P < 0.01$

Source: HEA Health and Lifestyles Survey, 1992

***Fig. 7.14.* Odds ratios of current smoking by measures of socioeconomic position: for men and women aged 16–74 years after controlling for age, social capital, health status and reported stress**

to those in social class I. Women in the highest social class are also least likely to be current smokers, but this class variation does not reach statistical significance after controlling for other factors in the model. However, women living in the most materially deprived conditions (as indicated by a high PDI score) have substantially higher odds of smoking compared to those who are materially advantaged, with a significant gradient in smoking also evident for men as their level of material deprivation increases.

Compared to the reference category of full-time workers, unemployment is associated with greater smoking for men only, whilst the odds of smoking are significantly reduced for men and women who are economically inactive and for women who work part time.

Discussion and conclusions

The results have shown that both social support and social capital are independently associated with health behaviour after controlling for the structural position of men and women. However, much less of the variation in diet is accounted for by social support than by social class and material deprivation. Similarly, smoking is less strongly associated with social capital and social support than with socioeconomic factors.

A lack of material resources strongly increased the likelihood of smoking or having a poorer than average diet for men and women, with these health-damaging behaviours more common among the lower social classes and the unemployed. This confirms previous work demonstrating the importance of socioeconomic resources in determining a healthy lifestyle (Cooper, Ginn and Arber, 1999; Marsh and McKay, 1994; Dowler and Calvert, 1995). There was some evidence that stress increased the likelihood of smoking among women after controlling for their socioeconomic position, but stress did not influence diet quality.

Those with adequate social support are least likely to have an unhealthy diet, whilst a lack of social support from friends and relatives increases the likelihood of smoking, particularly among women. These findings support work based on German survey data (Hartel, Steiber and Keil, 1988) showing that increased social ties and contacts reduce the likelihood of smoking after adjusting for age, gender and educational level. We found no evidence that stress can account for the greater smoking and poorer diet of men and women who lack social support.

Chapter 6 showed that social capital, as indicated by perceptions of the quality of the neighbourhood, was significantly associated with the health status of women but not men after controlling for other factors (Table 6.6). Neighbourhood social capital is also a significant determinant of health behaviour among women only; low neighbourhood social capital is associated with smoking. This suggests that the quality of the social environment has a more important influence on women than men, in terms of both their health and health behaviour. However, the beneficial effect of community activity in decreasing the likelihood of smoking applied to both men and women. Gottlieb and Green (1984) reported that smoking behaviour was reduced among men and women with regular church attendance after controlling for structural factors, and these authors suggest that social control may account for the positive influence of community activity on health behaviour.

The finding that the divorced/separated were more likely to smoke and that being previously married was associated with a poorer quality diet and smoking among some groups suggests that being married can have a positive influence on health-related behaviour (Broman, 1993; Umberson, 1992; Cooper, Ginn and Arber, 1999). Previous research has suggested that the benefits of marriage on health behaviour are mediated by social support or shared socioeconomic resources. The loss of support from a spouse through marital dissolution or death may worsen health behaviour, at least in the short term. In contrast, our results show that differences in health behaviours between the married and non-married remain after adjusting for socioeconomic differences and variation in perceived social support.

8. The effect of social support on the health and smoking behaviour of older people

It has been argued that social support becomes more important for maintaining good health with advancing age (Minkler, 1984). Changes in the lives of older people, such as retirement, widowhood and relocation, may disrupt established sources of social support or bring about changes in the type of social support given and received. The presence of supportive social networks may 'buffer' the individual against adverse health outcomes or health-damaging behaviour or serve to reduce stress and improve self-esteem, which ultimately benefit health and health behaviour (see Part I).

Research in this area has tended to neglect older age groups in favour of those under the age of 65 years, even though the size and availability of social networks have been shown to vary with age (Kahn, 1979; Phillipson *et al.,* 1998). There is evidence to suggest that social support networks differ for men and women (Shumaker and Hill, 1991) and these gender differences may be particularly marked in later life. For example, the greater longevity of women means that they are more likely to become widowed, live alone and experience greater material deprivation and disability than men of the same age (Arber and Cooper, 1999; Arber and Ginn, 1991). All of these factors may contribute to lower social support and greater feelings of social isolation, which may be detrimental to health and health-related behaviour.

Socioeconomic position is strongly associated with the physical health status and health-related behaviour of older age groups (Cooper, Ginn and Arber, 1999). Those from lower social classes and income groups are more likely to report chronic illness, poor general health and functional disability (Arber and Cooper, 1999), and smoking is greatly increased relative to the higher socioeconomic groups (Cooper, Ginn and Arber, 1999; Arber, Cooper and Ginn, 1999). However, although social support has been found to be positively associated with health and health behaviour among older people (Broman, 1993) the relative contribution of social support compared to structural factors in influencing health and health behaviour requires further investigation.

This chapter uses nationally representative data from the 1994 General Household Survey (Bennett *et al.*, 1996) to assess the role of social support and structural factors in relation to the general health and smoking behaviour of older people aged 65 and above.

There is some debate about what constitutes social support for older age groups, with some authors arguing that statutory support services are most important for maintaining good health (Minkler, 1984). Our analysis of the GHS shows that the overall use of three voluntary or statutory services (meals on wheels, lunch club and day centre) is very low among those aged 65+ at approximately 8%. However, the use of these services is strongly associated with functional disability for older men and women (Table 8.1). It is therefore not possible to assess the direction of causation between health and the use of these services using cross-sectional data.

Table 8.1. Percentage of men and women using statutory/voluntary services* by level of functional disability, aged 65+

	Level of functional disability					
	None	Slight	Moderate	Severe	All	*P* (Sig)
Men	2	7	14	20	6	< 0.001
N =	(806)	(338)	(168)	(123)	(1435)	
Women	3	8	15	24	9	< 0.001
N =	(894)	(482)	(349)	(301)	(2026)	
All	2	8	15	22	8	< 0.001
N =	(1700)	(820)	(517)	(424)	(3461)	

*Includes meals on wheels, lunch club and day centre
Source: General Household Survey, 1994

Our measure of social support is based on visits to and visits received from friends and relatives, as well as contact with neighbours (see Appendix C). These measures can be used to assess social connections with others (Barrera, 1986), but the GHS data give no indication about the quality of the social contact. It is not possible to examine older people's contact with friends, children and other relatives separately, which is an important limitation, as these types of contacts are likely to be differentially motivated and to have a different meaning for the older person. For example, contact with friends is usually voluntary, whereas family ties are often based on a sense of obligation (Antonucci, 1990). Our analysis of the HEA Health and Lifestyles Survey in Chapter 6 suggests that social support from friends is more important for health than contact with relatives.

As our measure of social support is based on meeting friends and relatives, they are likely to be influenced by the level of functional disability and the chronic health status of older people. For example, impaired mobility will limit the ability to go out and visit others, whereas visits made to the home by friends and relatives may become more frequent as a result of the older person's poor health and need for assistance. Due to the problems in establishing the direction of causation between visiting patterns and limiting long-standing illness or functional disability, our study uses respondents' own assessment of their general health in the last year. This provides an indicator of subjective wellbeing.

We use measures of functional disability, socioeconomic position and frequency of visits as independent variables in our analysis to try and assess the extent to which level of disability, social circumstances and contact with neighbours, friends and relatives contribute to the subjective health status of older age groups. We then analyse the association of social and structural factors with smoking behaviour.

It is unlikely that all older people will have equal access to social support networks, so we begin by examining variation in older people's contact with neighbours, friends and relatives.

The distribution of social support among older age groups

The availability and composition of socially supportive networks are not evenly distributed among older people. Kahn (1979) first suggested that individuals are surrounded by a 'convoy' of significant others during their lifetime, and that the composition of the convoy varies with age. Findings from survey data generally show that the social networks of older people are smaller than for younger age groups, but that older women report more close social contacts than older men (Phillipson *et al.,* 1998).

Over two-fifths of older people have frequent contact with their neighbours, 40% of older women and 46% of older men see their neighbours nearly every day to talk to. Having no contact at all with neighbours is more common among women than men.

Table 8.2 shows that the frequency of visits to friends and relatives decreases with advancing age, but the frequency of visits by friends and relatives does not vary significantly with age. Over half of older people aged 65+ visit their friends and relatives at least weekly, and in each age group this is more likely for older women than men. However, visiting friends is strongly associated with age for both sexes; only 15% of men and 20% of women aged 85+ visit more than once a week, compared with over one-third of men and women in their late 60s. Conversely, the proportion of older people who do not visit friends and relatives increases consistently with age for men and women, from 11% aged 65–69 years to 35% of men and 43% of women aged 85 and above (Table 8.2(a)).

Receiving visits from friends and relatives does not vary significantly by age for older people (Table 8.2(b)) and all but a small proportion of men and women in each age group receive some visits. Those aged 85+ are most likely to receive more than one visit a week from friends and relatives, particularly among older women.

The age-related decline in visits to friends and relatives and the increase in visits received from these sources is likely to reflect increasing levels of chronic ill health and functional disability among older people, particularly older women. The nature of social contact may change with age; visits to the older person's home become more frequent and may be increasingly focused on practical assistance, whilst restricted mobility is likely to make travelling to visit friends and relatives more difficult.

Figure 8.1 shows the percentage of older men and women who do not visit friends or relatives according to their marital status. Single older men seem particularly isolated, being unlikely to visit and receive visits from friends and relatives. Widowed older women and divorced/separated older men are less likely to visit than the married, particularly for men.

Figure 8.2 shows that twice as many single women as widows receive no visits: 10% compared with 5% lack this type of social support. This could suggest differences in the *type* of social support received by widows rather than the lack of social support *per se*. Approximately one-quarter of single and divorced older men do not receive visits from friends and relatives, with a much lower proportion among the married and widowed (Figure 8.2). The greater propensity of married men to both receive and make visits to friends and relatives suggests that marriage is important in maintaining social contacts whereas single and divorced/separated older men are much less likely to have either source of social contact. In all, single older men are the most isolated in terms of lack of visits made or received.

Previous research on older people suggests that a lower socioeconomic position is associated with reduced social contact. Figure 8.3 shows that the frequency of visits to friends and relatives is strongly associated with income for both sexes. Those in the top income quintile are most likely to visit friends and relatives more than once a week, whilst older people on the lowest income are much more likely to report that they do not visit friends and relatives at all. This supports results from US survey data (Krause and

Table 8.2. Social support based on frequency of visits to and from friends and relatives by age group: men and women aged 65+

	Men						Women					
	65–69	70–74	75–79	80–84	85+	All 65+	65–69	70–74	75–79	80–84	85+	All
65+												
(a) Visits to friends/ relatives												
More than weekly	36	32	25	25	15	30	40	39	40	28	20	36
Once a week	23	24	21	20	17	22	21	23	15	17	11	19
Within last month	23	22	21	17	24	22	21	17	17	22	14	18
Not within last month	7	9	11	8	9	7	7	6	9	8	12	8
Do not go to visit	11	13	22	30	35	17	11	16	20	26	43	19
%	100	100	100	100	100	100	100	100	100	100	100	100
N =	474	461	238	179	87	1 439	557	605	374	278	220	2 034
(a) Visits from friends/ relatives												
More than weekly	40	35	35	42	46	38	43	49	48	44	52	47
Once a week	21	23	27	26	21	24	24	21	22	23	20	22
Monthly or less	32	35	32	24	28	31	27	24	23	28	23	25
Do not receive visits	7	7	6	8	6	7	5	6	7	5	5	6
%	100	100	100	100	100	100	100	100	100	100	100	100
N =	475	461	238	178	87	1 439	558	605	374	277	220	2 034

Visits to friends and relatives: $P < 0.001$ for men and women
Visits from friends and relatives: P (ns) for men and women
Source: General Household Survey, 1994

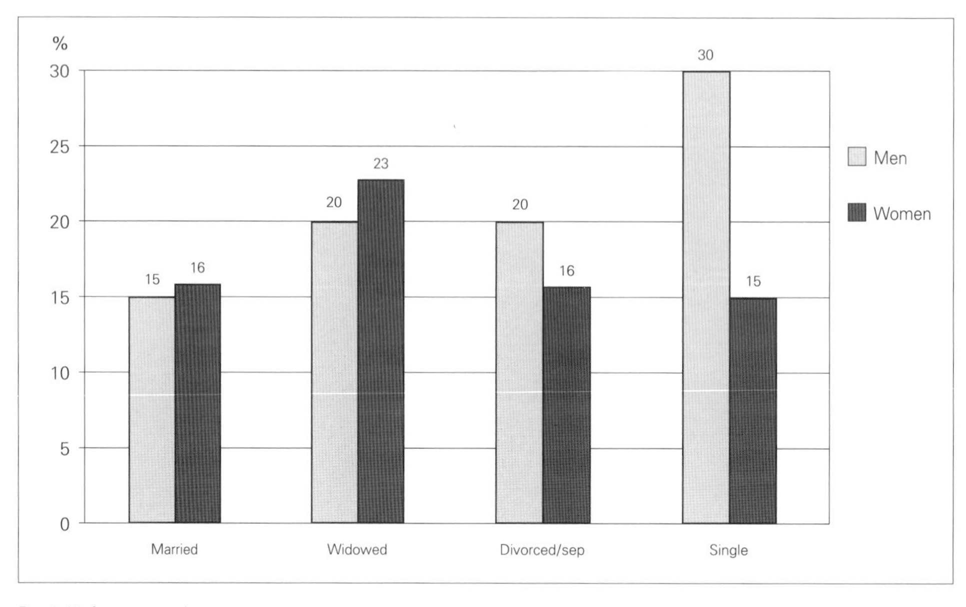

P < 0.01 for men and women
Source: General Household Survey, 1994

***Fig. 8.1.* Percentage who do not visit friends or relatives by marital status: men and women aged 65+**

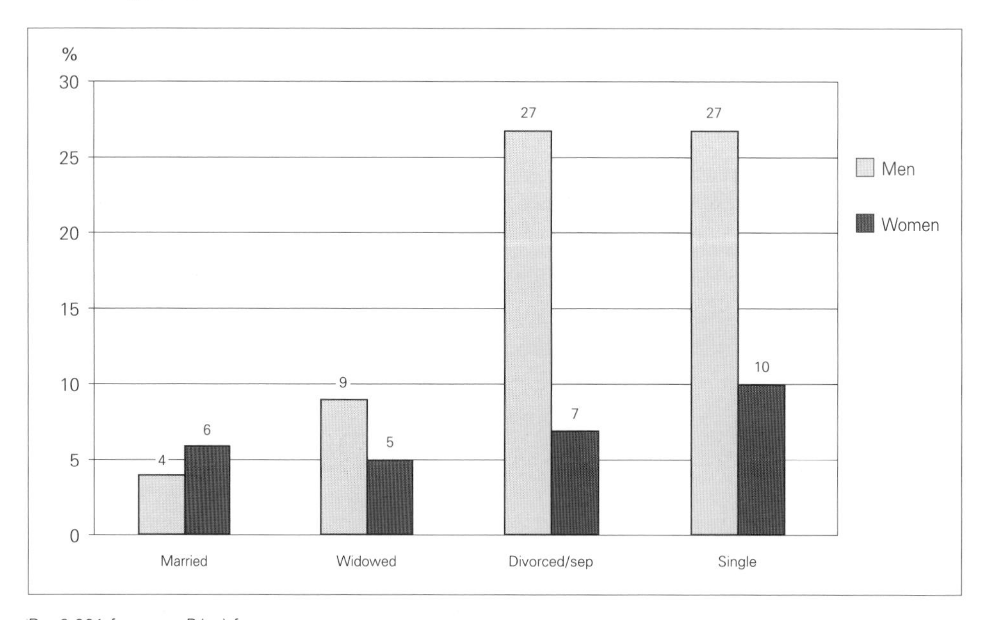

P < 0.001 for men; *P* (ns) for women
Source: General Household Survey, 1994

***Fig. 8.2.* Percentage who do not receive visits from friends or relatives by marital status: men and women aged 65+**

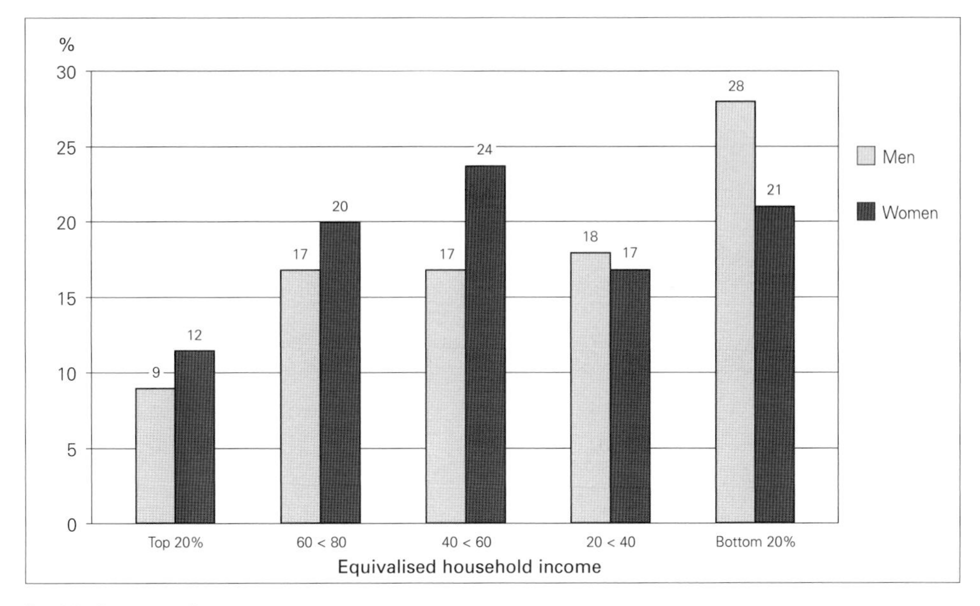

$P < 0.01$ for men and women

Source: General Household Survey, 1994

***Fig. 8.3.* Percentage who do not visit friends and relatives by equivalised household income: men and women aged 65+**

Borawski-Clark, 1995) and suggests that financial resources may influence the ability of older people to maintain this type of social interaction. The effect of low income in limiting outside social contact may be as great as that of disability or the loss of a spouse in later life. However, we are unable to assess whether the relationship between social support and socioeconomic resources differs using other indicators of social support, such as quality of social contact (Krause and Borawski-Clark, 1995) or when contact with friends and relatives is examined separately (Lang and Carstensen, 1994), because this data is unavailable in the GHS.

Social support, socioeconomic position and health

Previous research on the links between social support and the health of older people has tended to focus more on mortality than on self-reported health status (Minkler, 1984) and among younger people there has been a preoccupation with the relationship between social support and mental rather than physical health status (see Bloom, 1990).

Figure 8.4 shows that the frequency of visits to friends and relatives is significantly associated with the general health of older men and women. The percentage reporting good health consistently decreases as visits to friends and relations become more infrequent. The proportion with good general health is halved among those who make no visits at all to friends and relatives compared to those who do so more than once a week. Frequent social contact may therefore promote a sense of wellbeing, but poor health is also likely to reduce the feasibility of visits to friends and relatives.

The relationship between visits received from friends and relatives and self-assessed health is less consistent (Figure 8.5). For men aged 65–74 years there is no variation in reported health status, but men aged 75+ who receive visits are more likely to report good health, although this is not statistically significant. Older women who have received visits from friends and relatives in the last month are more likely to report good health; among those with no visits, only 31% aged 65–74 and 15% aged 75+ report good health.

Figure 8.6 shows that contact with neighbours is positively related to self-assessed health. Over 40% of older people who see their neighbours to chat to once a week or more report good health, compared with approximately 30% for those who have no such contact. However, as with contact with friends and relatives, it is impossible with cross-sectional data to assess the direction of causation between health status and social contact.

These results could indicate that frequent contact with neighbours, friends and relatives is important in promoting good general health among older men and women. Those lacking visits from friends and relatives or who never visit them have poorer self-assessed health. However, it is important to consider other possible confounding factors, such as an increasing level of functional disability that may make social contact with others outside the home more difficult. For example, Figure 8.7 shows the percentage of older men and women who do not see their neighbours, according to their level of functional disability. The functional disability scale used is based on the ability to perform everyday tasks (see Appendix C). Contact with neighbours who live nearby is clearly reduced as functional impairment becomes more severe. Among those with no disability, only a small proportion do not see their neighbours; this increases to approximately 22% among those with a moderate impairment and is greatest for older women who are severely impaired at 30%.

Older people's sense of wellbeing is likely to reflect the material conditions in which they live, including housing (Arber and Ginn, 1991). Figure 8.8 shows how the health of older people varies according to whether they live in owner occupied, rented or local authority accommodation. Local authority tenants are much less likely to report good health than those in privately rented or owner occupied housing, which is likely to reflect the more disadvantaged socioeconomic position of this group. For owner occupiers and local

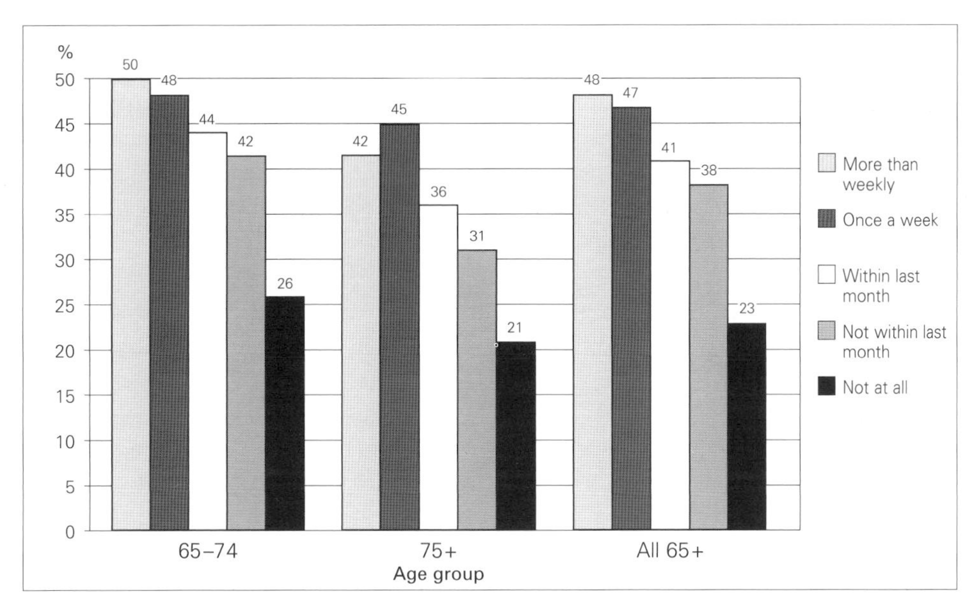

Men

$P < 0.001$ for all age groups

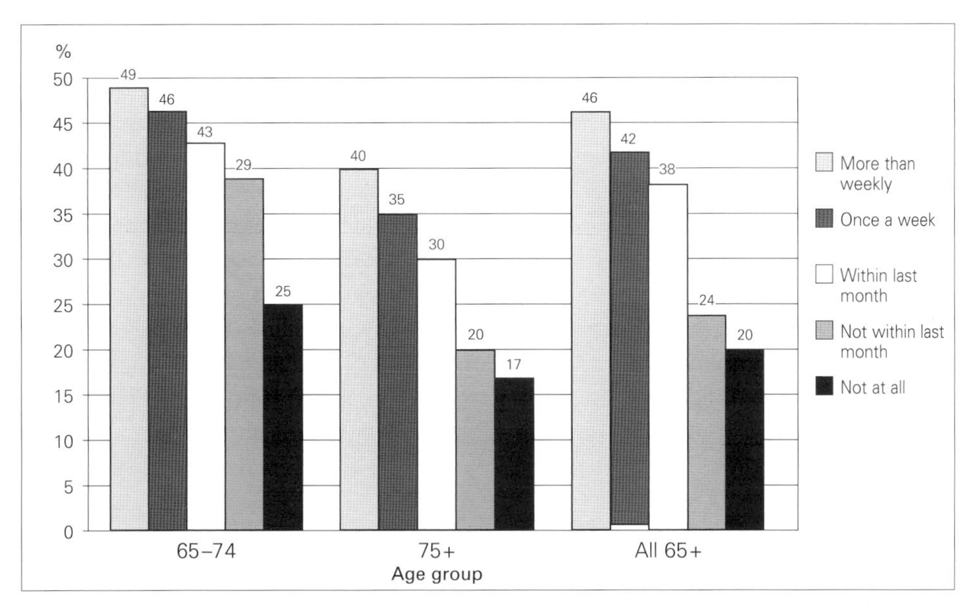

Women

$P < 0.001$ for all age groups

Source: General Household Survey, 1994

***Fig. 8.4.* Percentage reporting good health by frequency of visits to friends and relatives: men and women aged 65+**

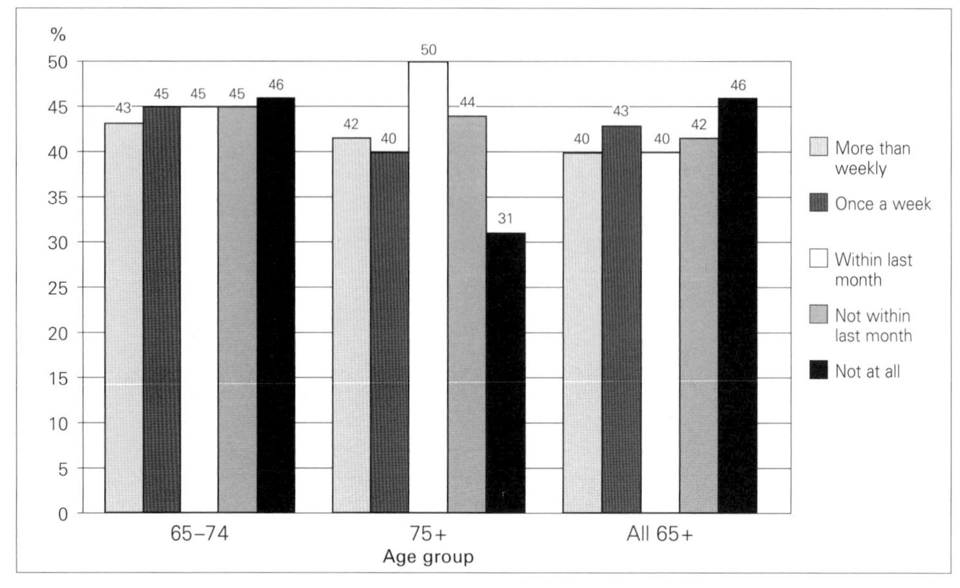

Men

P (ns) for all age groups

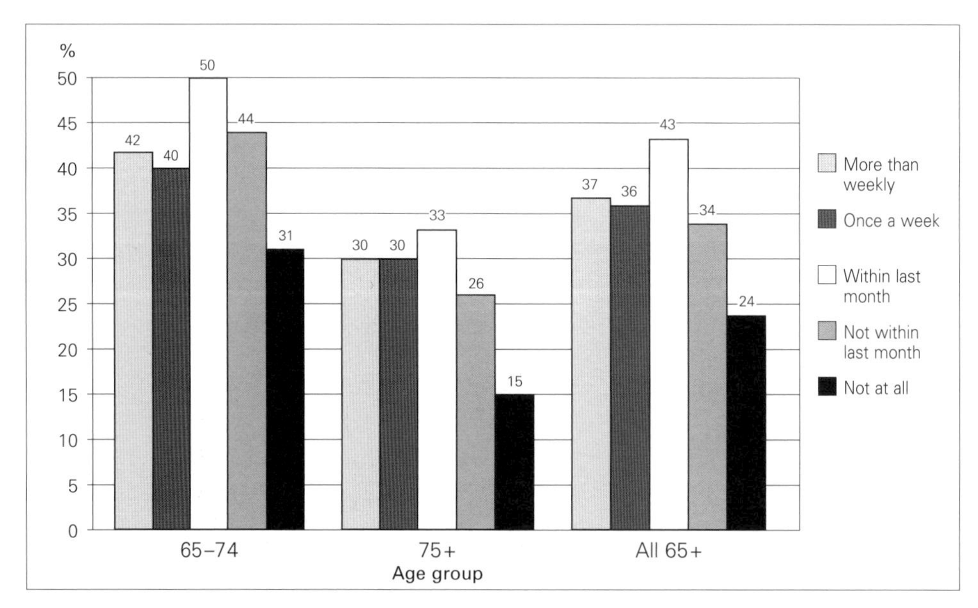

Women

$P < 0.001$ for 75+ and all 65+. P (ns) for 65–74

Source: General Household Survey, 1994

***Fig. 8.5.* Percentage reporting good health by frequency of visits received from friends and relatives: men and women aged 65+**

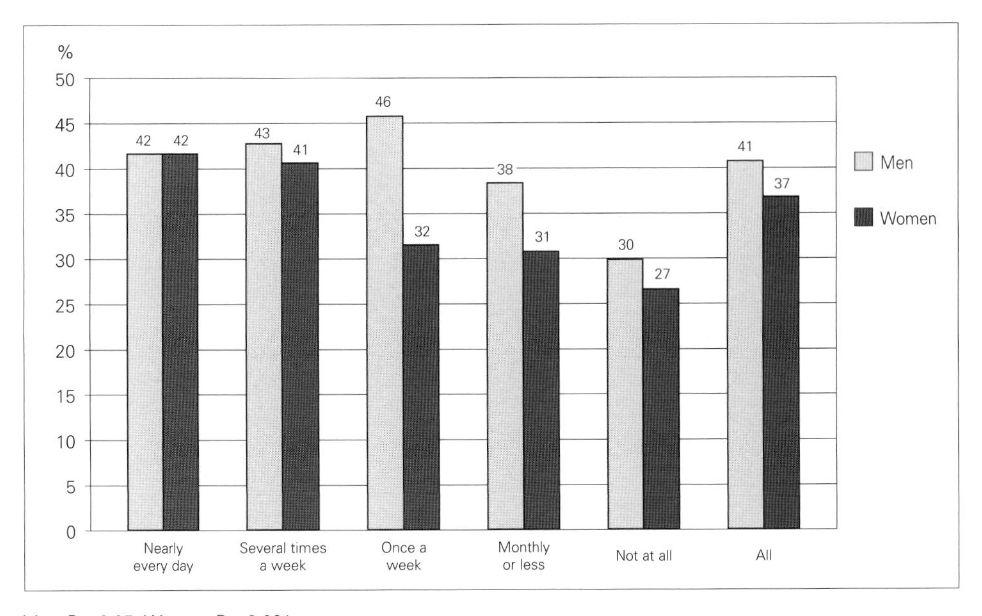

Men $P < 0.05$; Women $P < 0.001$

Source: General Household Survey, 1994

***Fig. 8.6.* Percentage reporting good health by frequency of contact with neighbours: men and women aged 65+**

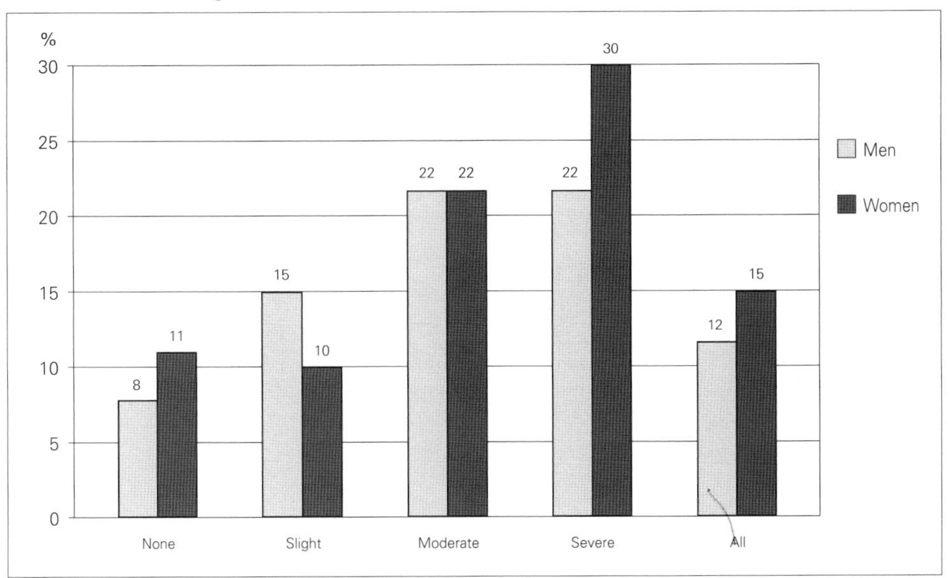

$P < 0.001$ for men and women

Source: General Household Survey, 1994

***Fig. 8.7.* Percentage who do not see neighbours to chat to by level of functional disability: men and women aged 65+**

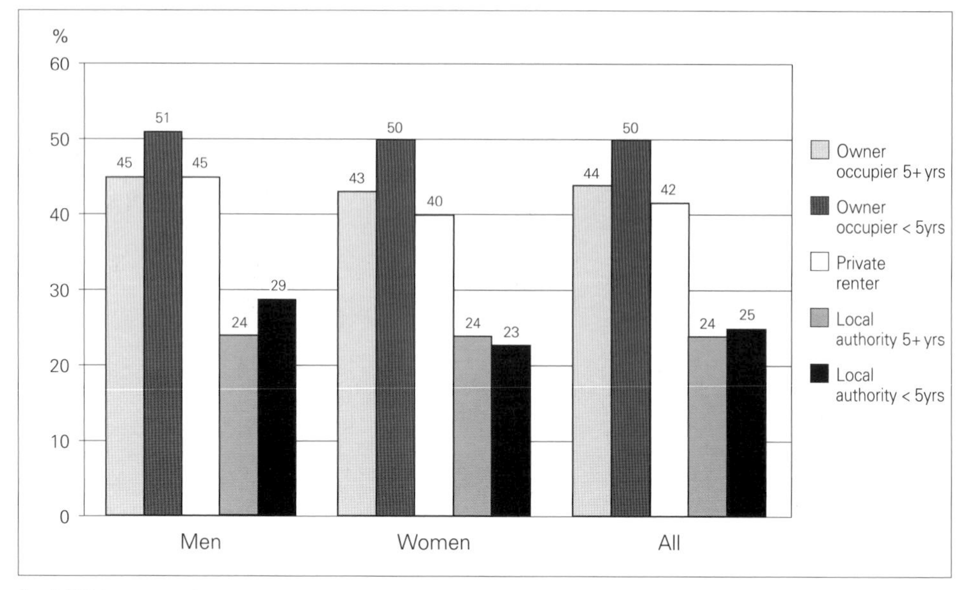

P < 0.001 for men and women
Source: General Household Survey, 1994

***Fig. 8.8.* Percentage reporting good health by length of time in current housing and tenure: men and women aged 65+**

authority tenants a distinction is made according to whether the older person has moved in the last five years. Relocation may be prompted by retirement, or increased disability may make moves to sheltered housing or to live with relatives more likely. These moves may have a disruptive influence on available social support. However, there is no evidence of this: older people in owner-occupied housing and men living in local authority housing for less than five years are more likely to report good health than longer-term residents in the same type of housing.

There are clear social class differences in self-assessed health for older men and women based on their last main occupation (Figure 8.9), confirming previous findings (Arber and Cooper, 1999). Approximately 25% more men and 15% more women aged 65+ who were previously employed in a professional or managerial occupation rate their health as 'good' than those previously in a semi- or unskilled occupation, with women who have never worked also much less likely to report good health. These differences between the manual and non-manual classes are evident for all age groups and are particularly marked for older men in their late 60s and early 70s and for women aged 75–79 years.

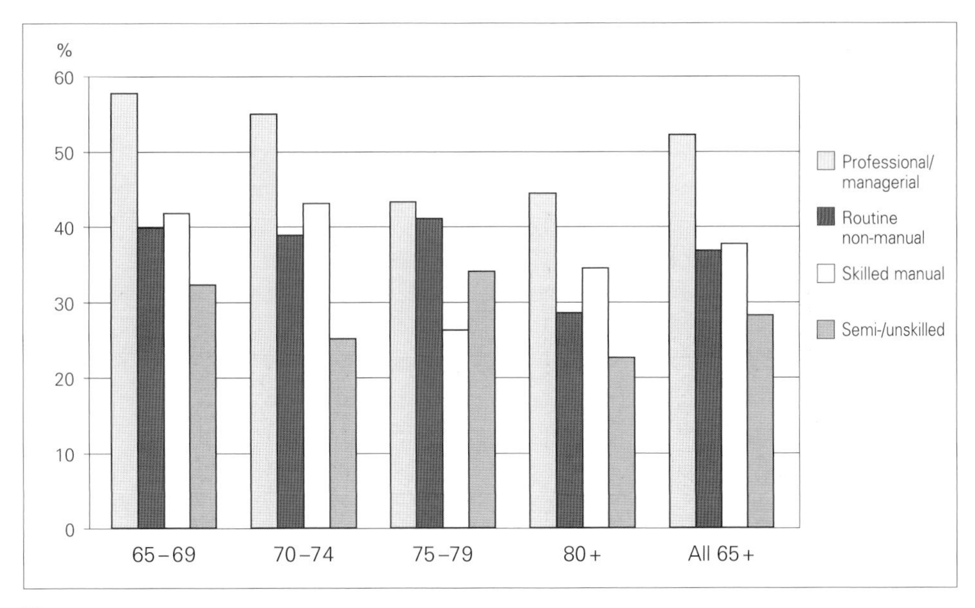

Men

Men aged 65–69 and 70–74 $P < 0.001$; 75–79 and 80+ P (ns)

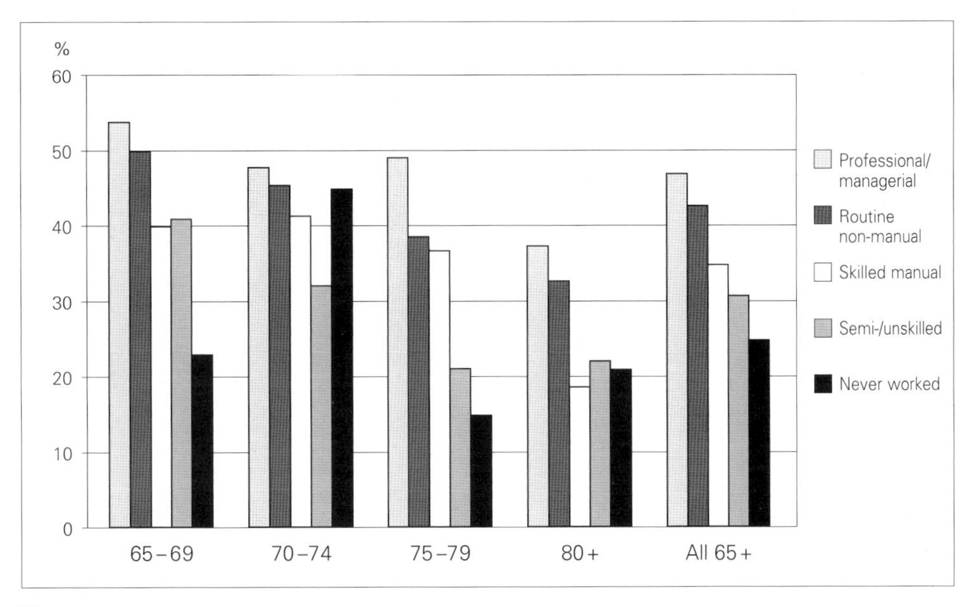

Women

Women aged 65–69, 70–74 and 80+ $P < 0.05$; 75–79 $P < 0.01$

Source: General Household Survey, 1994

Fig. 8.9. **Percentage of men and women reporting good health by age group and socioeconomic group***

*Actual percentages are listed in Appendix E.

Social support, socioeconomic position and smoking

In addition to having poorer self-assessed health, older men in the lower socioeconomic groups are approximately twice as likely to smoke cigarettes as men in the non-manual classes in each age group (Figure 8.10). For women aged 65–74 and 75+ there is no consistent class variation in smoking. Our results are likely partly to reflect cohort differences in smoking behaviour, as suggested by the clear decline in smoking with advancing age (see Figure 7.9, p. 105). Older women who smoke are less class divided than older men.

Cigarette smoking varies significantly among older people according to their living arrangements (Figure 8.11). Nearly 40% of older men and nearly one-quarter of older women who are divorced/separated are current smokers, which falls to approximately 15% among older people who are married. Smoking is also higher among single men relative to the married but is lower among single women aged 65 and above. Older people who are widowed and living with others are more likely to smoke than older people who are widowed and living alone. This association between divorce/separation and increased smoking has been reported elsewhere for older people (see Cooper, Ginn and Arber, 1999) and our findings are consistent with the hypothesis that marriage has a positive influence on health behaviour, particularly for men (Umberson, 1987, 1992).

In addition to marital status, individuals with access to supportive social relationships have been shown to engage in less health-damaging behaviour (Berkman and Breslow, 1983; Gottlieb and Green, 1984). Broman (1993) found that supportive relationships with friends reduced smoking after controlling for age, education and the level of income of men and women. However, this American study did not include those aged 65 and above. Friends or family members may encourage healthier behaviour or exert social control over acceptable behaviour, although it would be misleading to assume that social relationships always promote a healthier lifestyle (see Part I).

Figure 8.12 shows the percentage of older people currently smoking cigarettes by the frequency of visits received from friends and relatives. There is no increase in smoking among older women as the frequency of visits decreases, but twice as many older men who do not receive any visits are smokers compared with those who receive visits more than once a week. There is also some evidence that smoking is greater among men who do not go out to visit friends and relatives, but this is not statistically significant (Figure 8.13). There is no variation in smoking among older women according to their frequency of visits to friends and relatives. There is some evidence to suggest that older people who

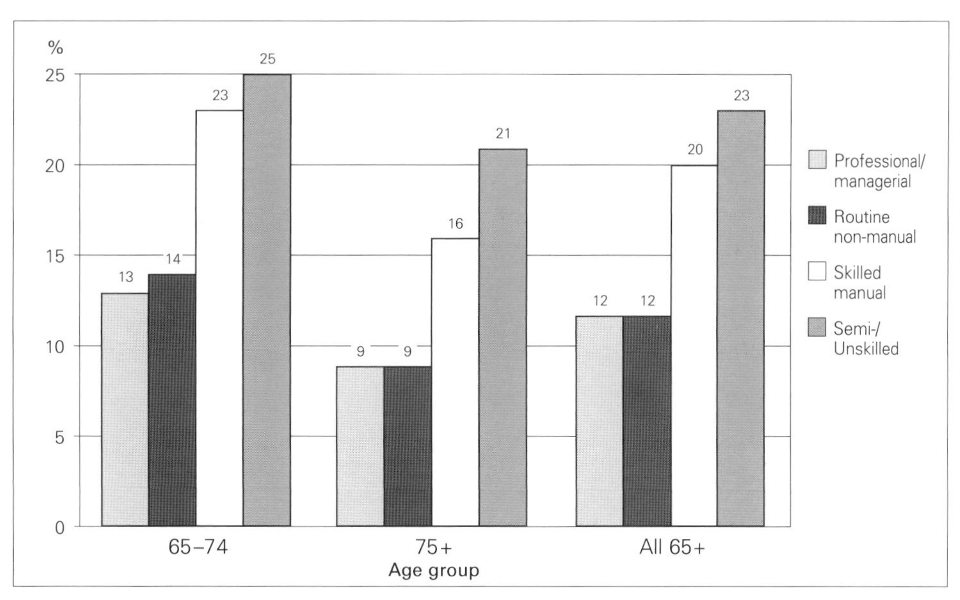

Men

Men aged 65–74 $P < 0.01$; 75+ P (ns); All 65+ $P < 0.001$

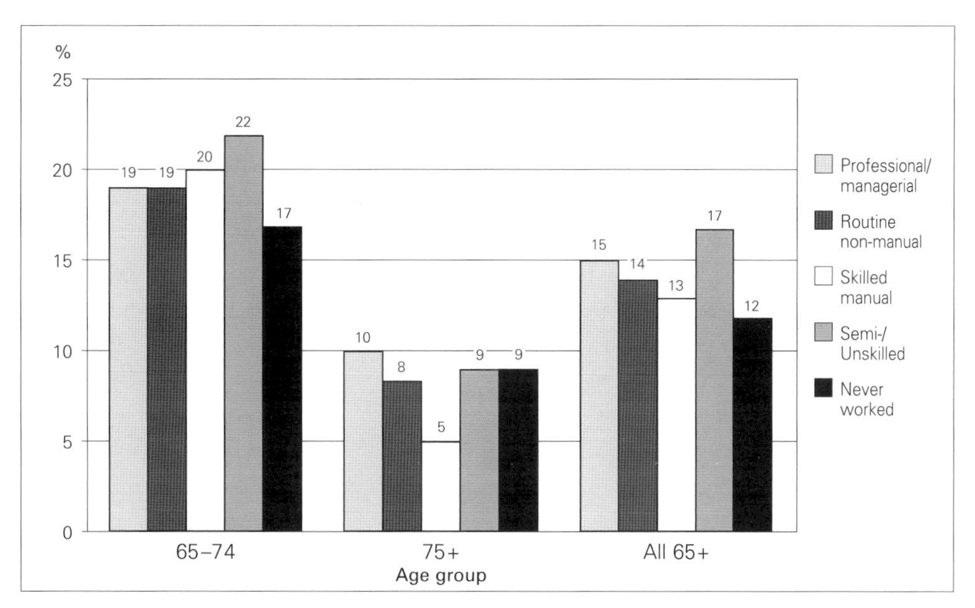

Women

Women in all age groups P (ns)

Source: General Household Survey, 1994

***Fig. 8.10.* Percentage of men and women currently smoking cigarettes by age group and socioeconomic group**

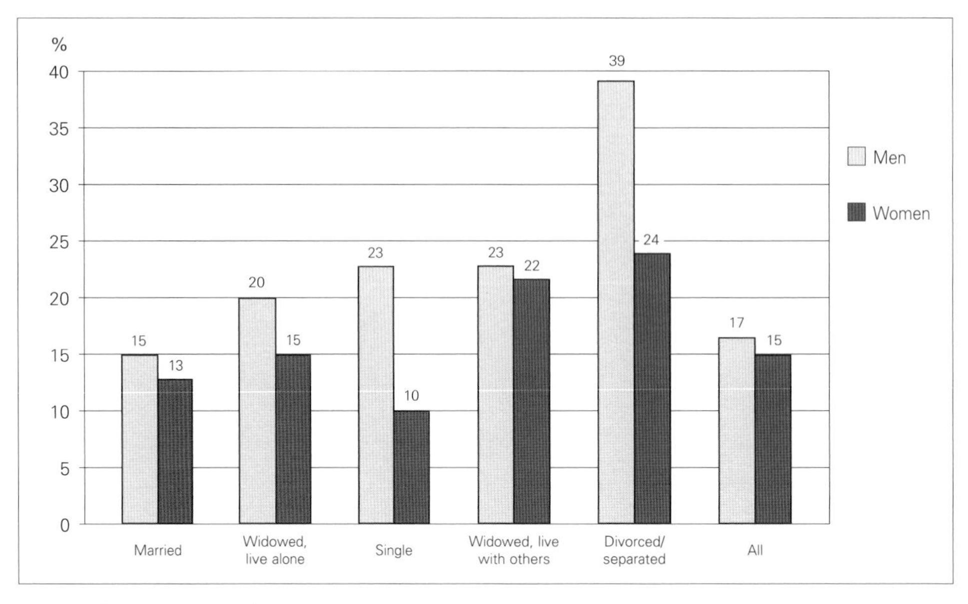

P < 0.001 for men; *P* < 0.01 for women
Source: General Household Survey, 1994

***Fig. 8.11.* Percentage currently smoking cigarettes by living arrangements: men and women aged 65+**

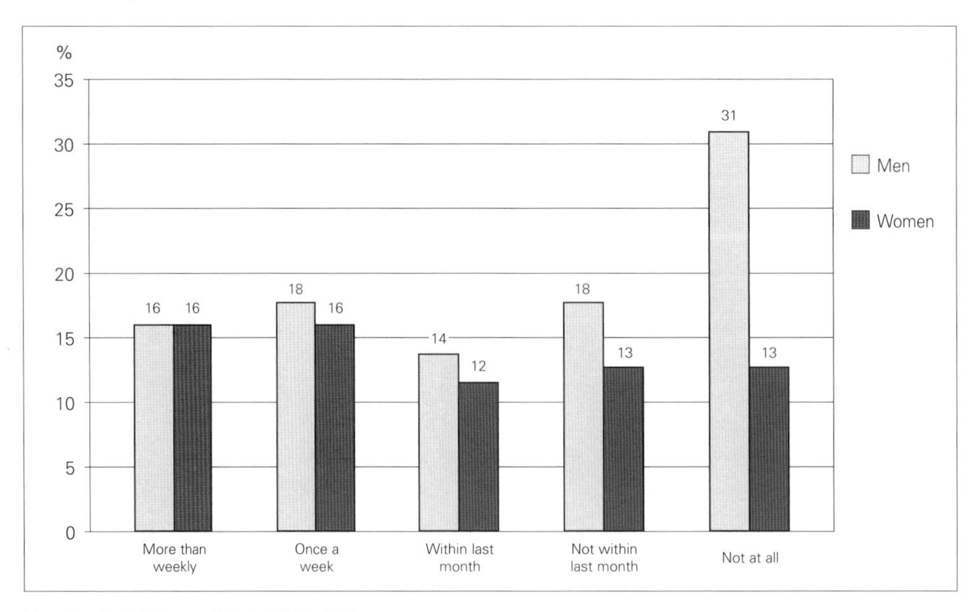

Men *P* < 0.01; Women *P* (ns); All *P* < 0.05
Source: General Household Survey, 1994

***Fig. 8.12.* Percentage currently smoking by frequency of visits received from friends and relatives: men and women aged 65+**

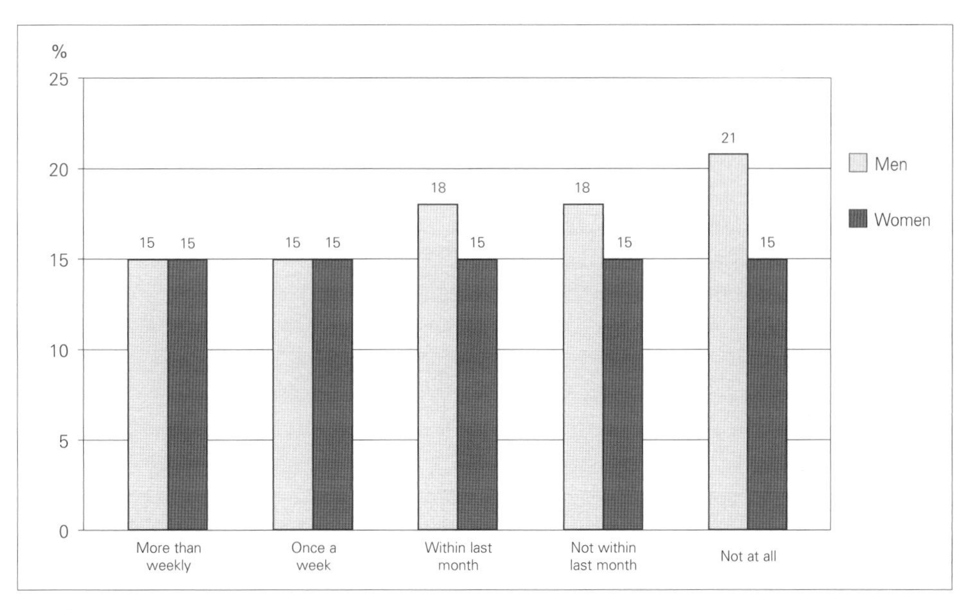

P (ns) for men and women

Source: General Household Survey, 1994

***Fig. 8.13*. Percentage currently smoking by frequency of visits to friends and and relatives: men and women aged 65+**

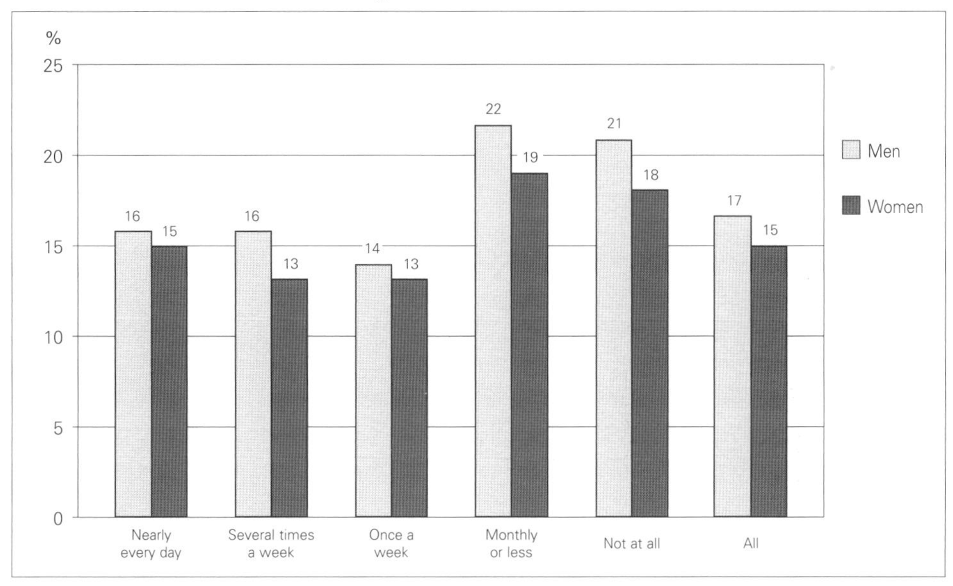

P (ns) for men and women

Source: General Household Survey, 1994

***Fig. 8.14*. Percentage currently smoking cigarettes by frequency of contact with neighbours: men and women aged 65+**

see their neighbours less than once a month or do not see them at all are more likely to smoke than those who see neighbours at least once a week (Figure 8.14), but these results are not statistically significant.

Summary

Social support, in terms of visits to and from friends and relatives, shows significant variation among older people, with the likelihood of visits to friends and relatives decreasing with advancing age and lower income. Being married is positively associated with social support, with older men who are single or divorced/separated being most likely to lack contact with friends and relatives.

Regular contact with neighbours, friends and relatives is associated with good general health after controlling for age and there was some evidence that older men who do not visit friends and relatives are more likely to smoke than those who visit more frequently. Older men and women in the lower socioeconomic groups were less likely to rate their health as 'good' than the more advantaged social groups and were also more likely to smoke.

Multivariate analysis

Using multivariate logistic regression analysis we will, first, examine the relative contribution made by social support and socioeconomic position to the self-assessed health of older people and, second, assess how these factors are associated with smoking in later life. For example, we have shown above that older people who do not visit friends and relatives are least likely to report good health, but it is uncertain whether this can be directly attributed to the absence of social contact or whether these men and women are more likely to be socioeconomically disadvantaged. In addition, the older person's level of functional disability is associated with the frequency of social contact and self-assessed health status. It is therefore important to control for both socioeconomic position and functional disability to assess whether our measures of social support are independently associated with self-assessed health.

We first present logistic models showing the likelihood of reporting 'less than good' health, and second, models showing the likelihood of being a current cigarette smoker. A series of three models are presented separately for men and women, due to gender differences in smoking and reported health status in later life, as well as differences in the structural position and social support networks of older men and women. Only those variables that reach statistical significance in the final model are presented.

Self-assessed health of men and women aged 65+

Using general health as the dependent variable, the first model examines the initial association between social support and health status after controlling for age-related differences and living arrangements. Structural measures of social class, household income and housing tenure are then added to a second model to assess the relative contribution of social and structural factors to general health. The final model controls for older people's level of functional disability to investigate whether any health variation associated with social support can be accounted for by reduced mobility among older age groups.

Table 8.3 (Model 1) shows that older people in their late 70s and early 80s are most likely to report less than good health. Self-assessed health was not significantly associated with marital status and living arrangements; these are therefore not included in the models.

The relationship between social support and health for older people differs according to whether the measure is based on visits to, or visits received from, friends and relatives. For both men and women, the odds of reporting less than good health consistently increase as the frequency of visits to friends and relatives decreases (Model 1). Women who have visited less frequently than once a week and men who have not visited within the last month are significantly more likely to assess their health as less than good than those who visit several times a week. The odds of poor health are over three times as great for older men and women who do not visit friends and relatives at all compared to the reference category.

This contrasts with the effect of frequency of received visits. Men who receive visits more than once a week are more likely to report poor health than those who receive no visits (Model 1). For women, the relationship is more complex. The odds ratios of poor health are slightly higher among those who never receive visits and those receiving visits more than weekly. Women who have received visits within the last month are least likely to report poor health.

The results for men do not indicate that the absence of this type of social contact contributes to a poorer health status, rather they suggest that the receipt of visits from friends and relatives is a response to poorer health. The odds of poor health are also reduced for women who receive weekly or monthly visits from friends and relatives, but there is some indication that poor health is greater among those who do not receive any visits.

Table 8.3. Odds ratios for logistic regression of less than good general health: men and women aged 65+

	Men			Women		
	Model 1	**Model 2**	**Model 3**	**Model 1**	**Model 2**	**Model 3**
Age	ns	ns	ns	+	ns	ns
65–69	1.00	1.00	1.00	1.00	1.00	1.00
70–74	1.08	0.99	0.97	1.11	1.08	0.90
75–79	1.44*	1.37	1.14	1.44*	1.42*	1.04
80–84	1.53*	1.50	0.89	1.61**	1.52*	0.87
85+	0.98	0.89	0.44*	1.49	1.50	0.67
Receives visits from friends/ relatives	†	†	ns	†	ns	ns
More than weekly	1.00	1.00	1.00	1.00	1.00	1.00
Once a week	0.86	0.89	1.03	0.92	0.97	1.05
Within last month	0.90	1.00	1.20	0.62**	0.72*	0.93
Not within last month	0.71	0.74	0.97	0.75	0.80	0.98
Not at all	0.42**	0.42**	0.59	1.22	1.33	1.56
Visits to friends/relatives	†††	†††	ns	†††	†††	†
More than weekly	1.00	1.00	1.00	1.00	1.00	1.00
Once a week	1.13	1.17	1.18	1.09	1.12	0.88
Within last month	1.38	1.35	1.25	1.51**	1.49*	1.21
Not within last month	1.80*	1.74*	1.43	2.43***	2.58***	1.89*
Not at all	3.54***	3.23***	1.68*	3.01***	2.75***	1.38
Whether see neighbours to chat to	ns	ns	ns	†	†	ns
Yes	1.00	1.00	1.00	1.00	1.00	1.00
No	1.45	1.43	1.15	1.39*	1.37*	1.03
Socioeconomic group		††	†		†	ns
Professional		1.00	1.00		1.00	1.00
Routine non-manual		1.65*	1.58		1.11	1.16
Skilled manual		1.52**	1.38		1.33	1.36
Semi/unskilled		2.11***	1.91**		1.56**	1.48*
Never worked					2.06*	1.94*
Household income		ns	ns		††	††
Top 20%		1.00	1.00		1.00	1.00
60 < 80%		1.04	1.09		1.61**	1.37
40 < 60%		1.08	1.04		1.54*	1.33
20 < 40%		1.43	1.47		1.92***	1.91***
Lowest 20%		1.34	1.49		1.89***	1.95***
Length of time in current housing tenure		††	ns		†††	††
Owner 5+ years		1.00	1.00		1.00	1.00
Owner < 5 years		0.74	0.62		0.95	0.98
Renter		0.85	0.74		0.69	0.65
Local authority 5+ years		2.25**	1.39		1.89*	1.55
Local authority < 5 years		1.53*	1.35		1.78***	1.51**

continued on next page

Table 8.3. *continued*

	Men			Women		
	Model 1	**Model 2**	**Model 3**	**Model 1**	**Model 2**	**Model 3**
Degree of disability			†††			†††
None			1.00			1.00
Slight (score 1–2)			2.88***			2.04***
Moderate (score 3–5)			8.61***			6.56***
Severe (score 6–8)			11.40***			11.94***
Very severe (score 9–12)			25.29**			16.88***
ΔLLR (df)	54.8 (9)	62.7 (11)	147.5 (4)	38.4 (8)	85.7 (12)	124.1 (4)
N =	1227			1721		

Statistical significance of variable in the model, †$P < 0.05$; ††$P < 0.01$; †††$P < 0.001$.
Statistical significance of difference from the reference category, *$P < 0.05$; **$P < 0.01$; ***$P < 0.001$.
Variables not statistically significant for men or women in the final model: living arrangements, frequency of contact with neighbours.
Source: General Household Survey, 1994

Lack of contact with neighbours is associated with poorer health, but the results are only statistically significant for older women. Women who do not see their neighbours to chat to have their odds ratio of poor general health increased by 39% after controlling for age and contact with friends and relatives.

The addition of socioeconomic measures improves the fit of the model by 62.7 for men and 85.7 for women, as shown by the change in the Log Likelihood Ratio (LLR). There is a clear class gradient in reported general health for both sexes, with the professional and managerial group least likely to report poor health. Men previously employed in semi- and unskilled occupations and women who have never worked are significantly more likely to rate their health as less than good relative to this group (Model 2).

Self-assessed health is also strongly associated with income for older women but not older men. Women in the highest income group are most likely to report good health, with the odds ratio of less than good health increased in the lowest two income groups by 92% and 89% respectively after controlling for social class and the other variables in the model.

Older people living in local authority housing are more likely to report poor general health than long-term owner occupiers, with the greatest odds ratio among those who have been resident in local authority housing for a period of five years or more (Model 2).

Adding socioeconomic factors to the model does not change the pattern of relationships between social support and health, with the exception that the frequency of visits from friends and relatives is no longer significantly associated with the health of older women.

As expected, self-assessed health is more strongly associated with functional disability than with social support or structural factors, improving the fit of the model by 147.5 for men and 124.1 for women. For both sexes, there is a linear increase in the odds ratio of poor general health as the severity of functional impairment increases.

The association between social support and general health is considerably weakened after controlling for functional disability. Thus, the bivariate relationship found between self-assessed health and visits to and from friends and relatives is largely explained by variation in functional ability. However, whereas the odds of poor health decrease for men who receive infrequent or no visits, the odds ratio of poor health increases among those women who do not receive any visits from their friends and relatives once disability is added to the model. Although not statistically significant, this could suggest that the absence of this type of social support independently contributes to poorer self-assessed health.

The relationship between contact with neighbours and self-reported health also disappears once disability is included in the model, reflecting the strong association between neighbourly contact and functional disability seen in Figure 8.7. Unlike social support gained through contact with friends and relatives, this type of social contact does not appear to influence perceived health directly, which may be expected if the relationship is based more on proximity and less on shared interests or family ties.

The relationship between socioeconomic position and health is weakened when disability is included in the model, confirming previous work showing that disability is most prevalent among the lower socioeconomic groups (Arber and Cooper, 1999). However, older people in the semi- and unskilled class remain significantly more likely to report poor health than the professional/managerial class, along with older women who have never worked. Women living on a low income are significantly more likely to report less than good health after controlling for any differences in functional disability between income groups.

The association between local authority housing and poor health for men becomes non-significant when disability is included in the model, which is likely to reflect the greater disability among this group relative to those in owner occupied accommodation. Women who have lived in local authority housing for less than five years are significantly more likely to rate their health as less than good relative to owner occupiers.

Cigarette smoking among men and women aged 65+

To examine the correlates of smoking, age and living arrangements are first entered into a logistic regression model, as both of these socio-demographic variables have been shown to be strongly related to smoking among older age groups. A second model examines whether these relationships are weakened by controlling for social support. Finally structural measures are added to assess the relative contribution of social and structural factors to the likelihood of being a current smoker.

Table 8.4 (Model 1) confirms that the likelihood of smoking significantly declines for men and women with increasing age, particularly among women aged 75 and above. The current living arrangements of older people are strongly associated with smoking (Model 1). Older men who are married are least likely to be smokers, with the odds of smoking significantly increased among men who are widowers or single relative married men. Divorced/separated men have a three times higher odds of smoking than married men. For women, the odds ratio of smoking is significantly increased by 48% for widows who live alone and more than doubled for widows living with others, relative to the married. The odds are increased for divorced/separated women compared to married women, but these results are not statistically significant.

None of the three measures of social support added in Model 2 reaches overall statistical significance after controlling for age and living arrangements. However, the odds ratios for frequency of contact with friends and relatives are shown where one category of the variable reaches statistical significance or where a pattern is suggested in the results, although any conclusions based on odds ratios that are not statistically significant must remain speculative. However, there is some evidence to suggest that women who receive visits from friends and relatives once a week or more often are most likely to smoke, whereas the odds ratio of smoking is slightly increased for men receiving no visits (Model 2).

Turning to visits made to friends and relatives, the odds ratio of smoking is significantly increased by 74% for men and 68% for women who do not visit friends and relatives, with smoking least likely among those who go out several times a week (Model 2). This result could suggest that visits to friends and relatives reduces the likelihood of smoking among older people. Once socioeconomic variables are included in the model, smoking is no longer significantly associated with frequency of making visits for older men, although the odds of smoking are still greater for those visiting less frequently (Model 3). Women who never visit friends and relatives remain significantly more likely to smoke, although the odds decrease slightly when socioeconomic position is included in the model. This suggests that older people who do not visit friends and relatives are more likely to lack socioeconomic resources than those who make such visits.

Table 8.4. Odds ratios for logistic regression of current cigarette smoking: men and women aged 65+

	Men			Women		
	Model 1	Model 2	Model 3	Model 1	Model 2	Model 3
Age	†††	†††	†††	†††	†††	†††
65–69	1.00	1.00	1.00	1.00	1.00	1.00
70–74	0.66*	0.65*	0.58**	0.77	0.74	0.72
75–79	0.69	0.64	0.58*	0.49***	0.47***	0.45***
80–84	0.44**	0.40**	0.36***	0.18***	0.17***	0.15***
85+	0.08***	0.06***	0.05***	0.13***	0.10***	0.10***
Living arrangements	†††	†††	††	†††	††	†††
Married	1.00	1.00	1.00	1.00	1.00	1.00
Single	1.90*	1.68	1.33	0.97	0.98	0.93
Widowed living alone	2.13***	2.22***	1.90**	1.48*	1.45*	1.41
Widowed living with others	2.14	1.99	2.54	2.63***	2.45***	2.87***
Divorced/separated	3.56***	3.22***	2.03	1.89	1.82	1.73
Receives visits from friends/relatives		ns	ns		ns	ns
More than weekly		1.00	1.00		1.00	1.00
Once a week		1.03	1.07		0.99	1.03
Within last month		0.80	0.85		0.67	0.72
Not within last month		0.83	0.85		0.84	0.85
Not at all		1.42	1.43		0.72	0.75
Visits to friends/relatives		ns	ns		ns	ns
More than weekly		1.00	1.00		1.00	1.00
Once a week		1.10	1.12		1.19	1.19
Within last month		1.59	1.54		1.34	1.28
Not within last month		1.41	1.35		1.30	1.26
Not at all		1.74*	1.47		1.68*	1.59*
Household income			††			ns
Top 20%			1.00			1.00
60 < 80%			1.63			1.20
40 < 60%			1.58			1.53
20 < 40%			2.26**			1.52
Lowest 20%			2.83***			1.36
Length of time in current housing tenure			††			ns
Owner 5+ years			1.00			1.00
Owner < 5 years			1.67			0.63
Renter			1.89			1.05
Local authority 5+ years			2.63***			1.20
Local authority < 5 years			1.96***			1.44*
ΔLLR (df)	52.7(8)	11.6(12)	52.9(11)	87.4(8)	14.0(9)	15.4(12)
N =	1232			1728		

Statistical significance of variable in the model: †$P < 0.05$; ††$P < 0.01$; †††$P < 0.001$.
Statistical significance of difference from the reference category: *$P < 0.05$; **$P < 0.01$; ***$P < 0.001$.
Variables not statistically significant for men or women in the final model: contact with neighbours, socioeconomic group.
Source: General Household Survey, 1994

Smoking among older people was not significantly associated with socioeconomic group after including income and housing tenure in Model 3, and so these results are not shown. Smoking is strongly associated with income and housing tenure for men but not for women, improving the fit of the model by 52.9 for older men (Model 3). Men in the lowest two income groups have a two times higher odds of smoking than those in the top income quintile, but income is not significantly associated with the smoking behaviour of older women (Model 3).

Men and women living in owner-occupied housing are least likely to smoke, with the odds ratio of being a smoker significantly increased for men living in local authority housing relative to owner occupiers, particularly those who have been resident for five years or more. This is likely to reflect an association between smoking and material deprivation. For women, housing tenure does not reach overall statistical significance in the model, but the odds ratio of smoking is significantly increased by 44% among those living in local authority housing for less than five years.

The association between smoking and divorce/separation becomes non-significant for men after controlling for their socioeconomic position, and lone widows are no longer significantly more likely to smoke than the married. This suggests that at least part of the association between being a divorced/separated older male or a lone widow and smoking results from their disadvantaged socioeconomic position relative to married couples.

Discussion and conclusions

Our analysis shows that structural factors are more strongly related to the health and health behaviour of older people than our measures of social support.

Consistent with previous work on older age groups, smoking and poor self-assessed health are related to socioeconomic disadvantage (Cooper, Ginn and Arber, 1999; Arber and Cooper, 1998). Older people living in local authority housing are most likely to report less than good health, and low income is strongly associated with poor health among women but not men. For both sexes, those in the lower social classes are less likely to report good health than those previously employed in professional occupations.

Poor health is associated with infrequent visits to friends and relatives after controlling for socioeconomic position, but the relationship between self-assessed health and this type of social support is largely explained by variation in functional ability among older people. Older men and women with functional impairment are less likely to go out to visit friends and relatives than those with no disability. This shows that social support in terms of visits to friends and relatives is largely dependent on the mobility and autonomy of older people. The more subjective indicator of perceived social support used in Chapter 7 (see Appendix B) is likely to be less strongly associated with disability.

However, after controlling for disability, older men who never visit friends and relatives and older women who have not done so within the last month remain most likely to report poorer health. This could suggest that the absence of this type of social support can be detrimental to their reported health status. The living arrangements of older people are not significantly associated with self-assessed health for men and women.

In contrast, smoking is strongly associated with living arrangements for older people, but the frequency of contact with friends and relatives is only weakly related to this health behaviour. Smoking among men is not significantly associated with social contact with friends and relatives after controlling for socioeconomic position. Married men are least likely to smoke, and smoking is significantly increased among the divorced/separated and widowers after controlling for differences in their social contact with friends and relatives. This supports findings suggesting that the marital relationship is important in promoting healthier behaviour among men (Cooper, Ginn and Arber, 1999; Umberson, 1992). However, after allowing for socioeconomic differences, only men who are widowed and living alone remain significantly more likely to smoke and there is no significant variation according to the frequency of visits to friends and relatives. This suggests that socioeconomic differences may exist between the married and the divorced/separated, the former having more access to shared material resources (Wyke and Ford, 1992) and that those who do not visit friends and relatives are more likely to lack financial resources than those who visit most frequently.

Unlike men, older women who do not visit friends and relatives are more likely to smoke after controlling for their living arrangements, income and housing tenure, which could suggest that the absence of social contact can be detrimental to health behaviour. Previous research suggests that smoking may function to alleviate stress and feelings of isolation (Graham, 1993), but there is no clear evidence that infrequent visits from friends and relatives increases smoking and our results suggest that the greater propensity to smoke among lone widows can partly be explained by their disadvantaged socioeconomic position relative to the married.

The association between widowhood and smoking found for older men and women after controlling for frequency of visits to and from friends and relatives and socioeconomic position is one which requires further investigation. The loss of a spouse has been found to be associated with greater psychological distress and lower perceived levels of social support (Umberson, 1992; Wyke and Ford, 1992). Our measure of social support includes no information as to the quality of that support, and there is no indicator of stress in the GHS to assess whether this influences the relationship between social support and smoking behaviour among older age groups.

Confirming previous research on older men and women (Cooper, Ginn and Arber, 1999), smoking is most strongly associated with structural measures; those in local authority housing are more likely to smoke than owner occupiers and older women living in low income households are most likely to be current smokers. These measures are more significant predictors of smoking than social class among people aged 65 and above.

9. Conclusions and recommendations

Age and gender are significant determinants of social capital and social support. With increasing age, men and women are more likely to have high levels of neighbourhood social capital and participation in community activity is greater among older women. This could reflect real differences between younger and older age groups in the quality of their living environment, or how that environment is perceived.

Measures of social support based on contact with friends and relatives show that women aged 16–74 years are more likely to report having close friends and relatives than men of the same age. Actual contact with friends decreases markedly with advancing age for both sexes, but this is not evident for contact with relatives. These results suggest that social contacts with friends and relatives may be differentially motivated, which highlights the value of measuring these contacts separately in social surveys. Among older people aged 65 and above, age significantly determined visits made to both friends and relatives, with visits decreasing as age advances, but the receipt of visits did not vary by age for older men and women.

However, interpreting age differences in social support using measures of social contact is problematic, firstly, because it does not account for differences in physical mobility which may restrict social activities outside the home and, secondly, because the actual pattern of social contact with others may change with age without lowering perceived social support. A more subjective indicator based on personal feelings about family and friends found the oldest and youngest age groups to be most likely to lack social support, with men in all age groups more likely to lack social support than women. We conclude that perceived closeness of social support from friends and relatives is more important than the actual amount of contact with these groups.

Social support and social capital also vary according to the socioeconomic characteristics of men and women. An association between unemployment and low neighbourhood social capital suggests that unemployed men and women are more likely to live in poor quality neighbourhoods lacking community facilities and resources than those in paid work. Being unemployed is also associated with a severe lack of perceived social support, particularly for men. For both sexes, perceived support from family and friends is most likely for those employed in professional occupations.

A consistent finding in all of our analyses is the strong association between health status and socioeconomic position. For men and women, those living in the most materially disadvantaged conditions, the unemployed and those in manual occupations are most likely to report a chronic illness or poor subjective health.

Smoking and unhealthy eating vary significantly according to age, and men are more likely than women to engage in these health-damaging behaviours. After adjusting for age differences, the likelihood of smoking and eating a poor quality diet is significantly greater among those who lack material and financial resources compared with the more advantaged social groups. These findings suggest that low income and insufficient material resources constrain food choice and that smoking is increasingly a marker for material deprivation among men and women.

Women are more likely to report stress than men, and high levels of stress are related to poor health for both sexes and greater smoking among women. There is no evidence that high levels of stress adversely influence quality of diet.

The influence of social capital and social support on health, stress and health behaviour is much weaker than the influence of socioeconomic factors, and these relationships differ for men and women.

Community activity and high neighbourhood social capital are associated with better health outcomes for both sexes. However, after controlling for socioeconomic factors, neighbourhood social capital is only significantly associated with reporting limiting long-standing illness and high levels of stress for women aged 16–74 years. Our results suggest that the association between poor general health and low social capital can largely be explained by the greater amount of stress experienced by women living in poor quality neighbourhoods.

Material living conditions and socioeconomic position remain much stronger predictors of adverse health than the perceived quality of the local area or involvement in community activities. However, there is some evidence to suggest that individuals living in materially deprived circumstances are also more likely to live in communities low in social capital;

the relationship between material deprivation and poor health is weakened by controlling for variation in neighbourhood social capital.

For both sexes, social support based on contact with friends is more strongly related to good health than contact with relatives, and this association remains after controlling for the amount of stress experienced by the individual. Among older people, our analyses show that frequency of contact with friends and relatives is likely to be largely dependent upon the physical mobility of men and women.

As well as being detrimental to health, poor material living conditions contribute to high levels of reported stress among those under 75 years of age. Importantly, no measure of social support was associated with stress after adjusting for socioeconomic characteristics of men and women. However, low neighbourhood social capital, being the victim of crime or attack or having lived in the area for a short period of time (1 year or less) were associated with significantly greater stress among women but not men. These results again suggest that women's surrounding environment can contribute to feelings of stress, but that stress is not significantly reduced by frequent or close contact with friends and relatives after controlling for age and structural characteristics.

Perceived social support from friends and relatives is associated with lower levels of smoking and a better quality diet after adjusting for the strong socioeconomic variation underlying these behaviours; individuals in all age groups with a severe lack of social support were more likely to be smokers and to have an unhealthy diet compared to those with adequate support from friends and family. However, among older adults aged 65+ there was little evidence to suggest that frequency of contact with friends and relatives was associated with smoking. Individual perceptions of social support from friends and relatives may be more relevant to understanding differences in smoking behaviour than measures based on the frequency of contact with these groups. Being divorced/separated is associated with smoking for all age groups, including for men and women aged 65 and above.

Neighbourhood social capital has a stronger influence on the smoking behaviour of women than men aged 16–74 years after controlling for differences in their socioeconomic circumstances and reported levels of stress. Women's chances of smoking consistently increase as neighbourhood social capital decreases, but there is no significant variation in men's smoking behaviour according to the level of social capital in their neighbourhood. Community participation is linked to lower smoking for both sexes, supporting previous research which suggests that 'social control' may have a role in regulating health behaviour (Gottlieb and Green, 1984).

Recommendations

This secondary analysis of existing survey data has derived indicators of social capital and social support and shown that both vary by age, gender and structural characteristics, such as employment status and social class. In future research, it is important to consider the relative influence of socio-demographic and structural factors on health and health behaviour when analysing the contribution of social support and social capital.

The three surveys used in our analysis contained different measures of social support, based on frequency of visits to and from friends and relatives (GHS), frequency of contact and perceived closeness of contact with friends and relatives (HALS) and perceived social support (HSE). Only the HEA Health and Lifestyles Survey contained information that could be used to measure social capital of the neighbourhood, based on community facilities and community involvement.

Our results showed that social capital and social support influenced health, reported stress and health behaviour differently according to how they were measured. More research is needed to validate existing measures of social support and social capital, for example, to explore how the meaning of 'close contact' and 'regular contact' with friends and relatives may differ for individuals depending on their age, sex, ethnic origin and social class, as well as other confounding factors, such as geographical proximity. Using measures of social capital and social support based on a scored response to a series of questions, it is important to ensure that the component items are gender neutral and do not contain an ethnic or class bias.

All of the surveys contained a social support measure based on contact with relatives, but this did not allow us to specify the nature of that relationship in any detail. Our analysis of the HALS suggested that social support from friends is more strongly related to health than social support from relatives, hence there is considerable value in collecting separate information about these types of social support.

None of the surveys contained measures of social trust or value of life that have been used in American and Australian surveys to conceptualise social capital (Bullen and Onyx, 1998; Putnam, 1996). More detailed questions which ask the individual to state who would provide social support on a day-to-day basis or during a crisis would limit the assumption that frequent social contact with friends and relatives is positively related to social support.

Appendices

Appendix A. Health and Lifestyles Survey, 1992

Social capital

Neighbourhood social capital

A summary measure of social capital was based on six questions which ask respondents about their neighbourhood:

Is it a place you enjoy living in?
Is it a place where you personally feel safe?
Is it a place where neighbours look after each other or not?
Has it good facilities for young children or not?
Has it good local transport or not?
Has it good leisure facilities for people like yourself or not?

Responses to these six questions were scored +1 if the answer was 'yes' and –1 if the answer was 'no'. A 'don't know' response was given a neutral score of 0. This gave a minimum social capital score of –6 and a maximum of 6. These responses were regrouped as follows:

Score –6–0	Low social capital
Score 1–2	Medium social capital
Score 3–4	High social capital
Score 5–6	Very high social capital.

For some analyses, the 'high' and 'very high' categories were combined.

Whether victim of crime or attack in last 12 months

Based on any 'yes' response to any one of these three events:

Personal experience of theft, mugging, break-in or other crime
Verbal abuse due to race or colour
Physical attack due to race or colour.

Length of time living in area

Recoded into four categories as follows:

1 10 or more years
2 4–9 years
3 2–3 years
4 1 year or less.

Community activity in last 2 weeks ('civic engagement')

Respondents are asked if they have done any of the following in the past fortnight:

Attended an adult education or night-class course
Participated in a voluntary group or local community group
Participated in community or religious activities.

These responses were counted to give a scale ranging from 0 (no community activity) to 3 (maximum community activity). This was then collapsed into a two-category variable:

1 No community activity
2 Engage in community activity (score is greater than 0).

Social support

Close friends and relatives

Respondents were asked if they had any close friends and close relatives that they see or speak to on a regular basis. The following variable was derived to reflect perceived *close* contact with friends and relatives;

1 Close contact with friends and relatives
2 Close contact with relatives only
3 Close contact with friends only
4 No close contact with friends or relatives.

Kin involvement in last 2 weeks

An indicator of involvement with relatives was constructed by counting how many of the following respondents had in the last two weeks:

Visited relatives
Had relatives visit them
Gone out with relatives
Spoken to relatives on the phone.

This gave a total ranging from 0 (no kin involvement) to 4 when respondents answered 'yes' to all of the above. The scale was combined into three categories:

1 4 contacts
2 2–3 contacts
3 0–1 contact.

Kith involvement in last 2 weeks

An indicator of involvement with friends was constructed by counting how many of the following respondents had in the last two weeks:

Visited friends
Had friends visit them
Gone out with friends
Spoken to friends on the phone.

This gave a total ranging from 0 (no kith involvement) to 4 when respondents answered 'yes' to all of the above. The scale was combined into three categories:

1 4 contacts
2 2–3 contacts
3 0–1 contact.

Socioeconomic position

Educational level

This was based on the highest educational qualification obtained and collapsed into five categories as shown below:

Educational level categories

1 Higher (degree or equivalent)	First and higher university degrees, prof. institute qualification Nursing qualifications: SEN, SRN, NNEB and higher diploma
2 A level or equivalent	GCE A level; City and Guilds advanced/final level; ONC/D, B/TEC Nursing general certificate or diploma
3 CSE/GCE O level or equivalent	CSE, GCE O levels; trade apprenticeship; clerical and commercial; City and Guild Craft/ordinary level/operative; craft technical certificate
4 Any other qualification	Insig Award Tech (GCIA); any other
5 None	No formal qualification.

Personal Deprivation Index (PDI)

An indicator of the material resources available to each individual was constructed by increasing the score by 1 for each of the following items that applied, giving a minimum score of 0 and a maximum score of 5. Those with a PDI score of 3 or more, which represents a high level of deprivation, were grouped together.

No central heating in household
No telephone in household
No car available
Home not owned
Income support/social security benefit received.

Employment status

Divided into the following four categories:

1 Employed full-time	Full-time, government training scheme
2 Employed part-time	Part-time

2 Unemployed *	For < 6 months or > 6 months; temporarily sick/disabled
3 Non-employed	Retired; at school or in full-time education; looking after the home; long-term sick/disabled.

Social class

Based on the Registrar General's classification. Five social classes as follows:

I
II
IIIN
IIIM
IV
V
Unclassified.

Social class information was only collected for respondents who were currently employed, retired or unemployed for less than 6 months. For the multivariate analysis, separate categories have been added to represent those who are long-term unemployed (6+ months), in education or training, sick/disabled or looking after the home, and classes IV and V have been combined.

Health status

General health

Respondents were asked to rate their health as very good, fairly good, fairly poor or very poor. We distinguish between those with very good health and those with less than very good health (the latter category includes any 'don't know' responses).

Limiting long-standing illness

Respondents were asked whether they had any long-standing illness, disability or infirmity, and those who answered 'yes' are asked if this limits their activities in any way. We use a two-category variable:

1 No limiting long-standing illness (includes those with non-limiting long-standing illness)
2 Limiting long-standing illness (LLI).

*Based on respondent's own assessment, not on whether actively seeking paid employment or hours worked per week.

Health behaviour

Cigarette smoking

This measure is based on current smoking status and does not include those who indicate that they used to smoke:

1 Do not smoke cigarettes at all
2 Smoke cigarettes.

Stress

Stress in last 12 months

Based on a self-assessed measure of stress or pressure experienced in the last 12 months:

1 Free from stress and pressure
2 Small amount of stress or pressure
3 Moderate amount of stress or pressure
4 Large amount of stress or pressure.

We have used the same four categories for our analysis and have focused on those experiencing a large amount of stress or pressure in the multivariate analysis.

Appendix B. Health Survey for England, 1993 and 1994

Social support

Social support is measured in the HSE by responses (true – score 3, partly true – score 2, not true – score 1) to the following seven questions in the self-completion section:

'There are people I know – amongst my family and friends – who . . .

1 do things to make me happy
2 make me feel loved
3 can be relied on no matter what happens
4 would see that I am taken care of if I needed to be
5 accept me just as I am
6 make me feel an important part of their lives
7 give me support and encouragement.

Possible scores ranged from 6 to 21, since the score was computed to allow a maximum of one item to be missing. An HSE-derived variable, PSSSCR2, grouped the scores:

21 No lack of social support
18–20 Some lack
6–17 Severe lack.

Living arrangements

Information on marital status and household composition was combined as follows:

Married
Cohabiting
Single alone
Widowed alone
Divorced/separated alone
Single with others
Widowed with others
Divorced/separated with others.

Socioeconomic position

Socioeconomic group

Based on the individual's current or last main occupation:

1 Managers/employers in large organisations, professionals
2 Managers/employers in small organisations, intermediate non-manual ancillary
3 Routine non-manual, intermediate non-manual supervisory
4 Skilled manual, manual supervisory, farmers (own account)
5 Semi-skilled manual, personal service, agricultural
6 Unskilled manual
7 Never employed.

Excluded: inadequately described, armed forces

Personal Deprivation Index (PDI)

An indicator of the material resources available to each individual was constructed by increasing the score by 1 for each of the following items that applied, giving a minimum PDI score of 0 and a maximum of 6. Those with a PDI of four or more, which represents a high level of deprivation, were grouped together:

No central heating in household
No telephone in household
No car in household
Home not owned
Unemployed (rather than economically inactive)
Income support received by anyone in household.

Health status

General health

Respondents were asked to rate their health in general as: very good, good, fair, bad or very bad. These responses were then collapsed into the following 3 categories:

1 Good
2 Fair
3 Bad.

Chronic illness

Respondents are asked if they have any long-standing illness, disability or infirmity. A 'yes' or 'no' answer to this question gave the following two-category variable:

1 No chronic illness
2 Chronic illness.

Health behaviour

Diet quality

A summary measure of diet quality, or Diet Score, was constructed from data in the HSE by applying Dowler and Calvert's (1995) method of scoring positively for each recommended item consumed (indicated in (a) below), and negatively for each 'go easy' item (indicated in (b)). However, because the HSE provides much less information on diet than was available to Dowler and Calvert, the Diet Score in this report cannot be compared directly with their Healthy Diet Score:

(a) Recommended items:
*bread, cereal, *vegetables, *fruit, *pulses — scored +1
(b) 'Go easy' items:
sugar in tea/coffee, *cakes, *biscuits, *sweets,
marg/butter, cooking oil, milk,
salt in cooking/at table — scored –1
(c) Neutral items — scored 0.

Account was taken in scoring of the type of bread (white 0, brown +1 or wholemeal +2), type of spread (whether butter –3, margarine –2 or reduced fat spread –1), type of cereal (whether high fibre +2), type of milk (whole –1, semi-skimmed 0 or skimmed +1). Frequency of consumption was scored where available (indicated by * in (a) and (b) above), from a maximum of +3 for recommended foods consumed daily to –3 for 'go easy' foods consumed daily.

The overall average diet score for men and women aged 16 and above was approximately zero, at 0.26. For the purposes of analysis, any individual with a positive diet score was classed as having a 'healthy diet' whilst a negative score indicated an 'unhealthy diet'. An example of the scoring used to classify diet is given below: Diet A shows a healthy diet and diet B is an example of an unhealthy diet.

Diet A	*Score*	*Diet B*	*Score*
Skimmed milk	+1	Whole milk	–1
Oil used in cooking	–1	Oil used in cooking	–1
Low/reduced fat spread	–1	Butter used	–3
Wholemeal bread	+2	White bread	0
High fibre cereal	+2	No cereal	0
Salt added in cooking	–1	Salt added in cooking	_1
Salt at table occasionally	–1	Salt at table generally	–2
No sugar in tea	0	Sugar in tea	–3
Cakes < 2 days/week	–1	Cakes 2–6 days/week	–2
Biscuits < 2 days/week	–1	Biscuits 2–6 days/week	–2
Sweets rarely	0	Sweets 2–6 days/week	–2
Vegetables daily	+3	Vegetables 5–5 days/week	+2
Fruit 5–6 days/week	+3	Fruit 5–6 days/week	+3
Bread daily	+3	Bread daily	+3
Diet score	+8		–9

Cigarette smoking

This measure is based on current smoking status and does not include those who smoke pipes or cigars or those who indicate that they used to smoke.

1 Do not smoke cigarettes
2 Currently smoke cigarettes.

Appendix C. General Household Survey, 1994: adults aged 65+

Social support

Going to visit friends or relatives

In the 1994 GHS, respondents aged 65 and over are asked whether or not they go to see or call in on friends or relatives at all. Those who answer 'yes' to this question are asked whether they do this every day, 2–3 times a week, once a week, 1–2 times each month or less than once a month. Those who indicate that they visit friends or relatives less than once a month are asked to state whether or not they went within the month preceding interview. Information from these questions was combined into the following categories to indicate different levels of social support:

1 More than weekly
2 Once a week
3 Within the last month
4 Not within the last month
5 Not at all.

Receiving visits from friends or relatives

Respondents are asked whether or not they receive visits from friends or relatives at all. Those who answer 'yes' to this question are asked whether they receive visits every day, 2–3 times a week, once a week, 1–2 times each month or less than once a month. Those who receive visits from friends or relatives monthly or less are asked to state whether or not they were visited in the last month. Information from these questions was combined into the following categories to indicate different levels of received social support:

1 More than weekly
2 Once a week
3 Within the last month
4 Not within the last month
5 Not at all.

Contact with neighbours

This measure is based on whether or not respondents see their neighbours (excluding friends or relatives) to chat to. Those who are in social contact with their neighbours are then asked to indicate whether they see them every day/nearly every day, 2–3 times a week, once a week, 1–2 times a month or less than once a month. This information was combined into the following categories:

1 Nearly every day
2 Several times a week
3 Once a week
4 Monthly or less
5 Not at all.

For some of the analysis, the following two-category variable has been used:

1 Contact with neighbours (codes 1–4 above)
2 No contact with neighbours (code 5 above).

Socioeconomic position

Length of time in current housing tenure

Information on the length of residency and housing tenure was combined for those living in owner-occupied and local authority housing. Owing to the small number of older people living in privately rented accommodation, we did not distinguish between long-term and short-term residents. The following groups were included in the analysis:

1 Owner occupier, 5+ years
2 Owner occupier, < 5 years
3 Private renter
4 Local authority, 5+ years
5 Local authority, < 5 years.

Socioeconomic group (SEG)

Socioeconomic group was based on the individual's own last main occupation. For women, those who had never been employed were included as a separate category:

1 Professional and managerial
2 Routine non-manual

3 Skilled manual
4 Semi- and unskilled manual
5 Never worked.

Income

Household income has been equivalised to take into account the number of adults in the older person's household. To create the equivalised scale, household income has been adjusted in the following way:

2 adults in household	No adjustment
1 adult in household	Divided by 0.6
3 adults in household	Divided by 1.5
4 adults in household	Divided by 2.

Living arrangements

Information on marital status and household composition was combined to distinguish between the widowed living alone and the widowed living with others. It was not possible to make this distinction for single and divorced/separated older people owing to the smaller numbers of men and women in these groups:

1 Married (includes cohabitees)
2 Single
3 Widowed, living alone
4 Widowed living with others
5 Divorced/separated.

Health status

General health

Respondents were asked to rate their health over the last 12 months as good, fairly good or not good. We distinguished between those reporting good health and those reporting fairly good or not good health:

1 Good health
2 Less than good health.

Functional disability

This scale is based on whether or not the respondents indicated that they were able to:

Get up and down steps
Get around the house
Get in and out of bed
Cut toenails themselves
Bath, shower or wash all over
Go out and walk down the road.

The scale has been used in earlier analyses of the GHS (see Arber and Ginn, 1991) in which these activities formed a Guttman scale. Each task was scored as follows:

0 On your own without difficulty
1 On your own, but with difficulty
2 Only with help from someone else, or not at all.

The resulting summated scale has scores ranging from 0 to 12. The scale has a reliability score of 0.82 using Cronbach's alpha, showing that the questions used to create the scale are internally consistent.

The scores were grouped into the following categories to represent the level of functional impairment. For some analyses, categories 4 and 5 are combined and referred to as 'severe', 6+.

1 None
2 Slight (score 1–2)
3 Moderate (score 3–5)
4 Severe (score 6–8)
5 Very severe (score 9–12).

Health behaviour

Cigarette smoking

This measure is based on the current smoking status of older people, and does not include those who smoke pipes or cigars or those who indicate that they used to smoke.

1 Do not smoke cigarettes
2 Currently smoke cigarettes.

Appendix D. Logistic regression: method and interpretation

Logistic regression enables a prediction to be made about the probability that an event will or will not occur, by reference to a comparative event. The main feature that distinguishes logistic regression from linear regression is that the dependent variable is dichotomous, for example, health is 'good' or 'less than good'.

Unlike the Least Squares method used in linear regression, the logistic method estimates the probability of an event occurring using the Maximum Likelihood method (ML). Coefficients from the data that make the observed results 'most likely' are selected for the model. The relationship between the independent variables and the probability is non-linear, hence an iterative method is used which produces probability estimates coded between 0 and 1.

The ratio of probability that an event will occur versus the probability that it will not is termed the odds. Applied to this report, odds ratios are used to demonstrate the log of the probability that an individual possessing certain characteristics will, for example, smoke (p) compared to the probability that a person with identical characteristics will not smoke. Odds ratios are presented for each variable included in the logistic model, indicating the log of the probability of smoking relative to a reference category, given a value of 1.0. For example, the reference category for marital status is 'married'. An odds ratio greater than 1.0 indicates that the probability of smoking is greater than for the reference category, whilst an odds ratio less than 1.0 reflects a lower probability of smoking than for the reference category.

For some of the analyses in Part II, the best-fitting logistic model has been selected using a 'Forward Stepwise' procedure. The first model tested contains only a constant term. At each step, the variable with the smallest significance level for the score statistic is entered into the model (the cut-off value is $P \leq 0.05$). All the specified variables in the blocks are then scaled for entry or removal using the likelihood ratio test (LR). For each variable, a log likelihood (–2LL) is calculated which demonstrates the effect of removing that variable from the model. If the resultant significance level is greater than the cut-off value then the variable is excluded from the final model.

To assess the relative degree of association of specific independent variables with the dependent variable, the change in Log Likelihood Ratio (LLR) is used. This improvement statistic represents the change in –2LL between successive steps of building a model and is comparable to the F-change test used in multiple regression.

Appendix E. Tables of percentages used in some figures

(Base numbers are given in brackets where appropriate)

Fig. 5.5 (p. 71) Perceived close contact with friends and relatives by marital status

	Married/ co-habiting	Single	Widowed	Divorced/ separated	All
(a) Men aged 16–74 years					
Both close friends and relatives	74	73	71	68	73
Close relatives only	16	8	16	17	14
Close friends only	6	15	5	11	9
No close friends or relatives	5	4	8	4	5
%	100	100	100	100	100
N =	1581	671	56	121	2430
(b) Women aged 16–74 years					
Both close friends and relatives	81	77	79	72	80
Close relatives only	11	7	10	10	10
Close friends only	6	15	8	13	8
No close friends or relatives	2	2	3	5	2
%	100	100	100	100	100
N =	1599	493	172	186	2450

Source: HEA Health and Lifestyles Survey, 1992

Fig. 5.6 (p. 72) Perceived close contact with friends and relatives by length of time living in area

	10+ years	4–9 years	2–3 years	1 yr or less	All
(a) Men aged 16–74 years					
Both close friends and relatives	76	72	65	60	73
Close relatives only	13	15	13	22	14
Close friends only	8	9	16	8	9
No close friends or relatives	3	5	6	9	4
%	100	100	100	100	100
N =	1549	483	237	213	2484
(b) Women aged 16–74 years					
Both close friends and relatives	82	78	79	70	80
Close relatives only	9	11	10	16	10
Close friends only	8	9	9	10	9
No close friends or relatives	2	3	2	5	2
%	100	100	100	100	100
N =	1517	564	209	227	2517

Source: HEA Health and Lifestyles Survey, 1992

Fig. 6.3 (p. 78) Neighbourhood social capital and health status

Neighbourhood social capital:	Low	Medium	High	Very high	All
(a) Men aged 16–74 years					
% with high stress	19 (641)	15 (644)	16 (703)	13 (408)	16 (2468)
% with less than good health	58 (641)	52 (644)	55 (710)	49 (482)	53 (2477)
% with limiting long-standing illness	15 (637)	15 (644)	14 (706)	13 (481)	14 (2469)
(b) Women aged 16–74 years					
% with high stress	28 (661)	19 (630)	20 (723)	15 (490)	21 (2504)
% with less than good health	57 (658)	54 (632)	53 (727)	46 (490)	53 (2507)
% with limiting long-standing illness	21 (659)	17 (628)	15 (717)	13 (490)	17 (2493)

Source: HEA Health and Lifestyles Survey, 1992
Base numbers in brackets

Fig. 7.6 (p. 99) Percentage of men and women with a healthly diet* by age and socioeconomic group

	16–34	35–54	55–74	75+	All 16+
(a) Men aged 16+ years					
Professional/managerial	54 (596)	58 (1208)	60 (717)	48 (176)	57 (2697)
Lower professional/managerial	44 (687)	51 (1060)	53 (619)	37 (140)	49 (2506)
Routine non-manual	37 (595)	45 (376)	52 (312)	33 (106)	42 (1389)
Skilled manual	28 (1352)	37 (1665)	39 (1443)	26 (310)	35 (4770)
Semi-skilled	27 (624)	34 (526)	38 (508)	25 (122)	32 (1780)
Unskilled	20 (203)	32 (157)	26 (178)	19 (36)	25 (574)
(b) Women aged 16+ years					
Professional/managerial	71 (359)	76 (375)	76 (164)	60 (42)	73 (940)
Lower professional/managerial	64 (846)	72 (1282)	74 (743)	51 (217)	69 (3088)
Routine non-manual	51 (1861)	64 (1878)	63 (1433)	47 (466)	58 (5638)
Skilled manual	49 (344)	58 (447)	55 (389)	41 (192)	53 (1372)
Semi-skilled	38 (1066)	52 (1130)	53 (966)	37 (395)	46 (3557)
Unskilled	33 (205)	45 (407)	52 (512)	29 (210)	43 (1334)
Never worked	46 (915)	55 (150)	55 (120)	40 (102)	48 (1287)

Source: Health Survey for England, 1993 and 1994

Base numbers in brackets
*Defined as a positive diet score (see Appendix B).

Fig. 8.9 (p. 129) Percentage of men and women reporting good health by age group and socioeconomic group

	65–69	70–74	75–79	80+	All 65+
(a) Men aged 65+ years					
Professional/managerial	58 (171)	55 (153)	43 (67)	44 (86)	52 (477)
Routine non-manual	40 (49)	39 (41)	41 (22)	29 (35)	37 (147)
Skilled manual	42 (165)	43 (163)	26 (99)	35 (87)	38 (514)
Semi-/unskilled	32 (92)	25 (103)	34 (47)	22 (49)	28 (291)
All	46 (486)	43 (467)	35 (238)	34 (265)	41 (1456)
(b) Women aged 65+ years					
Professional/managerial	54 (88)	48 (94)	49 (58)	37 (94)	47 (334)
Routine non-manual	50 (190)	45 (205)	38 (125)	33 (138)	43 (658)
Skilled manual	40 (48)	41 (56)	36 (40)	19 (43)	34 (187)
Semi-/unskilled	41 (202)	32 (220)	21 (123)	22 (169)	30 (714)
Never worked	23 (22)	45 (20)	14 (22)	21 (45)	25 (109)
All	46 (558)	41 (607)	33 (373)	27 (408)	37 (2036)

Source: General Household Survey, 1994
Base numbers in brackets

Appendix F. List of figures and tables

Figures

Tables

References

Antonucci, T C (1990). 'Social supports and social relationships', in: Binstock, R H and George, L K (eds). *Handbook of Aging and the Social Sciences,* 3rd edn. New York: Academic Press, pp. 205–26.

Arber, S. (1997) Comparing inequalities in women's and men's health: Britain in the 1990s. *Social Science and Medicine* **44**(6): 773–87.

Arber, S and Cooper, H (1999). Gender differences in later life: the new paradox? *Social Science and Medicine* **48**: 61–74.

Arber, S and Ginn, J (1991). *Gender and Later Life: A Sociological Analysis of Resources and Constraints.* London: Sage.

Arber, S, Cooper, H and Ginn, J (1999). 'Health inequalities in later life', in: Waller, S and Crosier, A (eds). *Seminar Series on Inequalities in Health*. London: Health Education Authority.

Barrera, M (1986). Distinctions between social support concepts, measures and models. *American Journal of Community Psychology* **14**(4): 413–45.

Belle, D (1987). 'Gender differences in the social moderators of stress', in: Barnett, R C, Biener, L and Baruch, G K (eds) *Gender and Stress*. New York: Free Press, pp. 257–77.

Bennett, N, Jarvis, L, Rowlands, O, Singleton, N and Haselden, L (1996). *Living in Britain: Results from the 1994 General Household Survey*. OPCS. London: HMSO.

Berkman, L F and Breslow, L (1983). *Health and Ways of Living: The Alameda County Study*. New York: Oxford University Press.

Bloom, R (1990). The relationship of social support and health. *Social Science and Medicine* **30**(5): 635–7.

Broman, C L (1993). Social relationships and health-related behavior. *Journal of Behavioural Medicine* **16**(4):1–17.

Bullen, P and Onyx, J (1998). *Measuring Social Capital in Five Communities in NSW.* http://www.mapl.com.au/A2.htm

Cobb, S (1976). Social support as a moderator of life stress. *Psychosomatic Medicine* **38**: 300.

Cohen, S (1988). Psychosocial models of the role of social support in the etiology of physical disease. *Health Psychology* **7**: 269–97.

Cohen, S and Willis, T A (1985). Stress, social support and the buffering hypothesis. *Psychological Bulletin* **98**: 310–57.

Coleman, J S (1988). Social capital is the creation of human capital. *American Journal of Sociology* **94**: supplement S95–S120.

Colhoun, H and Prescott-Clarke, P (eds) (1996). *Health Survey for England 1994*. London: HMSO.

Cooper, H, Ginn, J and Arber, S (1999). *Health-related behaviour and attitudes of older people: a secondary analysis of national data-sets*. London: HEA.

Cramer, D (1993). Living alone, marital status, gender and health. *Journal of Community and Applied Social Psychology* **3**: 1–15.

Dowler, E and Calvert, C (1995). *Nutrition and Diet in Lone Parent Families in London*. London: Family Policy Study Centre.

Ginn, J, Arber, S and Cooper, H (1998). Inequalities in older people's health behaviour: effect of structural factors and social relationships. *Journal of Contemporary Health* **7**: 77–82.

Gottlieb, N H and Green, L W (1984). Life events, social network, life-style and health: an analysis of the 1979 National Survey of Personal Health Practices and Consequences. *Health Education Quarterly* **11**(1):91–105.

Graham, H (1993). *When Life's a Drag: Women, Smoking and Disadvantage*. London: HMSO.

Greeno, C G and Wing, R R (1994). Stress-induced eating. *Psychological Bulletin* **115**(3):444–64.

Hartel, U, Steiber, J and Keil, U (1988). Social relations and smoking behavior: results from the first MONICA Survey Augsburg. *Sozial und Präventivmedizin* **33**(1): 27–31.

Health Education Authority (1995). *Health and Lifestyles: A Survey of the UK Population, Part 1*. London: Health Education Authority.

House, J S and Kahn, R (1985). 'Measures and concepts of social support', in: Cohen, S and Syme, L (eds). *Social Support and Health*. New York: Academic Press, pp. 83–108.

House, J S, Landis, K R and Umberson, D (1988). Social relationships and health. *Science* **214**: 540–5.

Kahn, R L (1979). 'Aging and social support', in: Riley, M W (ed.). *Aging from Birth to Death: Interdisciplinary Perspectives*. Boulder, Colo.: Westview Press, pp. 77–92.

Kawachi, I, Kennedy, B P and Lochner, K (1997). Long live Community: social capital as public health. *The American Prospect*, No. 35 (November–December): 55–9. Downloaded: pages 1–6. http://www.epn.org/prospect/35/35kawanf.html.

Kennedy, B P, Kawachi, I and Prothrow-Stith (1996). Income distribution and mortality: cross sectional ecological study of the Robin Hood index in the United States. *British Medical Journal* **312**: 1013–14.

Kessler, R C, Price, R H and Wortman, C B (1985). Social factors in psychopathology: stress, social support and coping processes. *Annual Review of Psychology* **36**: 531–72.

Krause, N and Borawski-Clark, E (1995). Social class differences in social support among older adults. *The Gerontologist* **35**(4): 498–508.

Lang, F R. and Carstensen, L L (1994). Close emotional relationships in later life: further support for proactive aging in the social domain. *Psychology and Aging* **5**(19): 315–24.

Marsh, A and McKay, S (1994). *Poor Smokers*. London: Policy Studies Institute.

McBride, C M, Curry, S J, Grothaus, L C, Nelson, J C, Lando, H and Pirie, P L (1998). Partner smoking status and pregnant smokers' perceptions of support and the likelihood of smoking cessation. *Health Psychology* **17**(1): 63–9.

McLeod, J D and Kessler, R C (1990). Socioeconomic status differences in vulnerability to undesirable life events. *Journal of Health and Social Behaviour* **23**: 220–4.

Minkler, M (1984). 'Social support and the health of the elderly', in: Cohen, S. and Syme, S L (eds). *Social Support and Health.* London: Academic Press.

O'Reilly, P (1988). Methodological issues in social support and social network. *Social Science and Medicine* **26**(8): 863–73.

Phillipson, C, Bernard, M, Phillips, J and Ogg, J (1998). The family and community life of older people: household composition and social networks in three urban areas. *Aging and Society* **18**: 259–90.

Putnam, R D (1993). The prosperous community: social capital and public life. *The American Prospect*, No. 13 (Spring 1993). Downloaded pages: 1–8.
http//www.epn.org/prospect/13/13putn.html

Putnam, R D (1996). The strange disappearance of civic America. *The American Prospect*, No 24. Downloaded pages: 1–17.
http://www.epn.org/prospect/24/24putn.html

Ross, C E and Mirowsky, J (1989). Explaining the social patterns of depression: control and problem solving – or support and talking? *Journal of Health and Social Behaviour* **30**: 206–19.

Runyan, D K, Hunter, W M, Socolar, R S, Amaya-Jackson, I, English, D, Lansverk, J, Dubowitz, H, Browne, D H, Bangdiwala, S I and Mathew, R M (1998). Children who prosper in unfavorable environments: the relationship to social capital. *Pediatrics* **101**: 12–18.

Sampson, R J, Raudenbush, S W and Earls, F (1997). Neighborhoods and violent crime: a multilevel study of collective efficacy. *Science* **277**: 918–24.

Shumaker, S A and Hill, D R (1991). Gender differences in social support and physical health. *Health Psychology* **10**(2): 102–11.

Skocpol, T (1996). Unravelling from above. *The American Prospect*, No. 25 (March–April 1996): 20–5. Downloaded pages: 1–7.
http://www.epn.org/prospect/25/25-cnt2.html

Stanton, W R and McGee, R (1996). Adolescents' promotion of non-smoking and smoking. *Addiction and Behaviour* **21**(1): 47–56.

Sterling, T D and Weinkam, J J (1985). The 'healthy worker effect' on morbidity rates. *Journal of Occupational Medicine* **27**(7): 477–82.

Townsend, P, Phillimore, P and Beattie A (1988). *Health and Deprivation: Inequality and the North.* London: Croom Helm.

Turner, R J and Avison, W R (1992). Innovations in the measurement of life stress: crisis theory and the significance of event resolution. *Journal of Health and Social Behavior* **33**: 36–50.

Umberson, D (1987). Family status and health behaviors. *Journal of Health and Social Behaviour* **28**: 306–19.

Umberson, D (1992). Gender, marital status and the social control of health behaviour. *Social Science and Medicine* **34**(8): 907–17.

Weiss, R W (1974). 'The provisions of social relationships', in: Rubin, Z (ed.). *Doing Unto Others.* Englewood Cliffs, NJ: Prentice-Hall,

Wilkinson, R G (1996). *Unhealthy Societies: The Afflictions of Inequality.* London: Routledge.

Wyke, S and Ford, G (1992). Competing explanations for associations between marital status and health. *Social Science and Medicine* **34**(5): 523–32.